PEOPLE USUALLY ONLY GLANCE AT A CLOCK...
...NOT ANYMORE!

Tracing our history and horological beginnings back over three centuries, we are a family company who understand what it takes to create the world's most exclusive and exciting interior timepieces.

We have installed timepieces in over 50 countries and continents, from the far east to the Middle East, Europe and Africa; from St Pancras International Railway Station to signature timepieces for the Waldorf–Astoria group.

Our pieces touch every sense and inspire you to be different. Don't miss the opportunity to define your next interior with something no one has yet seen. If you are looking for something special, then just take a moment to call our design team for a company briefing on the art, science and expression of time-telling from the world's best.

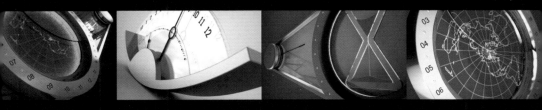

FORBES & LOMAX

THE INVISIBLE LIGHTSWITCH®

INTERIOR DESIGN YEARBOOK 2013

from the editor...

Welcome to the Interior Design Yearbook 2013; the consumer edition of our professional interior design sourcebook. Once again the book is published in association with the British Institute of Interior Design (BIID) which provides professional insight and a wealth of design experience to the book. Sue Timney, President, introduces the book and we have a full listing of the designer members of BIID at your disposal, should you wish to consult on design matters.

The Photo Casebook this year hosts an impressive array of designs from across the globe. Boutique hotels meet private chalets and penthouses as we explore the depths of the design world.

Such an emphasis has been placed on British design that it would be a loss not to continue the momentum into 2013. Designers are certainly embracing the concepts evolved in British design and in our *Design Spotlight*, the designers look at what epitomises great British design. We also consider subjects such as sourcing, International design, popular culture and the may other influences that help to shape design trends for the year ahead.

Our professional designers featured in this edition have all taken the time to divulge a little of their passion for the world of interior design. The team at John Cullen Lighting expose what it is to create a well-lit space and Tara Bernerd uses her extensive knowledge and expertise in hotel design to discuss how ideas and design concepts can be translated from the commercial to the residential.

If you have a passion for design and would like to learn more about the industry then our design education features should provide some insight into the ways in which you can take those first steps to becoming a fully qualified designer yourself.

It goes without saying that the designers who have contributed to this edition of the book are all at the top of their game and it is a pleasure to be able to include them within this book, sharing their expertise and encouraging you to get designing.

Jade Tilley
Editor

EDITOR
Jade Tilley
jade.tilley@onecoms.co.uk

PRODUCTION
Emma Coppin
emma.coppin@onecoms.co.uk

PRODUCTION ASSISTANT
Thom Luter
thomas.luter@onecoms.co.uk

ACCOUNT MANAGER
Audrey Stamp
audrey.stamp@onecoms.co.uk

ONLINE SALES
Danny Mehmet
danny.mehmet@onecoms.co.uk

CREDIT CONTROL
Carole Todd
carole.todd@onecoms.co.uk

MARKETING & PRESS
Louise Stupples
louise.stupples@onecoms.co.uk

WEB ENGINEER
Dean Woodford
dean.woodford@onecoms.co.uk

ADMINISTRATION
Joanne Cluer
joanne.cluer@onecoms.co.uk

SALES OFFICE MANAGER
Vicky Bullivant
vicky.bullivant@onecoms.co.uk

ASSOCIATE PUBLISHER
Donna Jenkins
donna@onecoms.co.uk

PUBLISHER & CEO
Robert J. Nisbet
robert@onecoms.co.uk

Interior Design Yearbook
1 Accent Park
Bakewell Road
Peterborough PE2 6XS
Tel: +44 (0) 1733 385300
fax: +44 (0) 1733 233794
www.onecoms.co.uk

contents

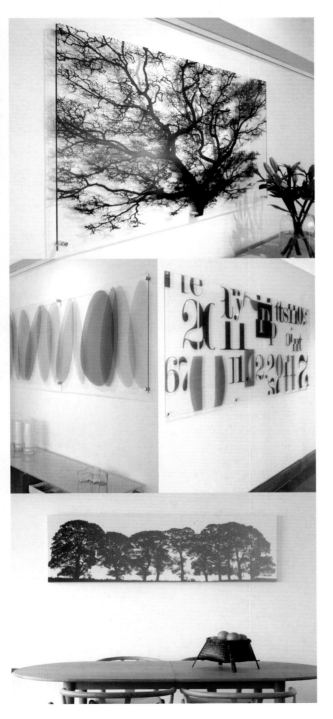

signarture ®
contemporary art + bespoke design

Established in Australia in 2006, and now available in the UK, Signarture is where contemporary art meets bespoke design.

We create artworks inspired by the trends in colour and design to complement contemporary interiors.

We reproduce our original artworks as uniquely transparent perspex art and covetable stretched canvases of superlative quality.

Choose from our comprehensive range online, or **customise by size and colour to meet your exact requirements.**

Visit our online gallery for all the inspiration you need and to **request a catalogue.**

Contact us for expert advice and to discuss your project.

+ 44 (0)20 7692 0600
artworks@signarture.com
78 york street | london | W1H 1DP
www.signarture.co.uk

deVOL Kitchens

FLOORS of STONE

Beautiful English furniture handmade in Leicestershire and luxurious natural stone flooring.
www.devolkitchens.co.uk | www.floorsofstone.com - Cotes Mill, Nottingham Road, Cotes, Leicestershire, LE12 5TL

INTERIOR DESIGN YEARBOOK 2013 *contributors*

Tara Bernerd
Founder,
Tara Bernerd & Partners
Tara is the founder of Tara Bernerd & Partners, a design consultancy offering a unique boutique service; guiding its clients through the entire creative stages, from initiating the ultimate concept to taking this through to a detailed design package.
www.targetliving.com

Scot R.Campbell
Principal, Tirmizi Campbell
Scot has a strong background in architectural management, problem solving and collaboration with project team members and consultants. Scot's strengths lie in his ability to lead a design team through all phases of a project from initial design concept to construction administration.
www.tirmizicampbell.com

Anna Dodonova
Founder, Anna Casa
Anna Dodonova is the founder of the Anna Casa design showroom, which exhibits exclusive, one-off pieces of luxury crafted furniture and lighting. The Kiev-born businesswoman began following her interior design dream in 2003 when she left a flourishing graphic design career in her adopted home of Berlin to retrain in London.
www.annacasa.net

Jacqueline Duncan
Principal,
Inchbald School of Design
Jacqueline founded the Inchbald in 1960, extending this to a Faculty in Garden Design in 1972. She previously managed the Michael Inchbald Studios.
www.inchbald.co.uk

John Evans
John Evans Interior
Architecture and Design Ltd
John is a Fellow of the Royal Society for the Arts, as well as being a Member of the Chartered Society of Designers and an active member of the BIID.
www.johnevansdesign.com

Alexandra Fry
Associate, John Cullen Lighting
Alex joined the lighting design team in 2002 and worked her way up to her current position of Associate. Alex's continued interest in design and detail has been recognised by her winning entry of Best Lighting Project at the idFX awards.
www.johncullenlighting.co.uk

Galina Ginzburg-Maly
Senior Project Designer, HBA
Following her graduation from Parsons School of Design, Gale gained several years experience at prestigious hospitality design practices in NYC. She then moved to London where she joined HBA two years ago.
www.hbadesign.com

Karen Howes
Co-Founder,
Taylor Howes Designs
Karen is the driving force and inspiration behind Taylor Howes Designs, a company, which has carved a unique niche in the interior design market through a comprehensive design service that the team offers to private clients and the commercial interior design industry.
www.taylorhowes.co.uk

Alan Hughes
Vice Principal, Inchbald School of Design
Alan's teaching experience includes five years at Middlesex University before joining Inchbald in 1991. After a period as Director of Visual Communication he took over the Directorship of the Architectural Interior Design Faculty and in 2002 he was appointed Vice Principal.
www.inchbald.co.uk

Nathan Hutchins
Senior Associate, HBA London
Nathan Hutchins gained his Masters in Architecture from the University of Washington, and shortly afterwards joined HBA, in its Los Angeles headquarters. Since coming to the UK in 2006, Nathan has headed up the design teams for some of HBA London's most prestigious projects throughout Europe, the Middle East, Africa and India.
www.hbadesign.com

Vincent Kirk
Managing Director,
KKE Architects
Vincent Kirk is an RIBA Architect, who studied at Huddersfield and London's South Bank Universities before forming KKE Architects in 2005. Vincent is a specialist in planning law and related areas, and serves on the Worcester City Council Conservation Area Advisory Committee.
www.kkearchitects.co.uk

Susan Knof
Senior Designer, SHH
Susan joined SHH in 2007. She has a BFA (Hons) from Miami University, where she majored in Interior Design. Susan was an Associate Professor at Berkeley College in the USA and has also done volunteer work for 'Habitat for Humanity International' in the USA and Hawaii.
www.shh.co.uk

Alix Lawson
Managing Director,
Lawson Robb
Alix studied Architectural interior Design at The Inchbald School of Design, London in 2000. Alix has over 10 years experience in the high-end residential market, as well as experience in Hotel Design. Her expertise lies in her in-depth knowledge of FF and e suppliers, products and her design direction of the company and projects undertaken.
www.lawsonrobb.com

INTERIOR DESIGN YEARBOOK 2013 *contributors*

Lucy Martin
Design Director,
John Cullen Lighting
Lucy, along with Sally, heads up the award winning John Cullen design team working on projects throughout the world. She contributes to national press articles, and also lectures regularly at design schools and interior events.
www.johncullenlighting.co.uk

Inge Moore
Principal, HBA London
Inge began her career in South Africa working in museum design. Since joining HBA London in 2001, Inge has been key in establishing the studio as one of the hospitality industry's most innovative and trendsetting interior design practices.
www.hbadesign.com

Sian Parsons
Senior Lighting Designer,
John Cullen Lighting
Sian started working for John Cullen in 2005 and is now a Senior Lighting Designer working on residential projects around the UK and was responsible for the project management of the new showroom at 561-563 Kings Road.
www.johncullenlighting.co.uk

Lindsey Rendall
Founder Rendall & Wright
Lindsey studied printed and woven textiles at the Surrey Institute of Art and Design before studying interior design with the KLC School of design. Lindsey went on to work at Designers Guild, before becoming Cameron Broom's principal designer. After six years in London, Lindsey teamed up with Helen Wright, an expert project manager within the interior design industry and together in 2006 founded Suffolk based design studio Rendall & Wright.
www.rendallandwright.com

Charlotte Rowe
Charlotte Rowe
Originally an art historian, Charlotte Rowe worked for some years in the creative and media industries in London and Sydney before gaining a post-graduate diploma in Residential Landscape and Garden Architecture at the Oxford College of Garden Design.
www.charlotterowe.com

Victoria Stainow
Founder, Victoria Stainow
Victoria designs a collection of bespoke furniture and lighting, inspired by classic mid-20th century design. The pieces are hand made in France by highly skilled craftsmen and can be altered in finish, dimension and material to create an individual, unique result.
www.victoriastainow.com

Sally Storey
Design Director, John Cullen
and Lighting Design
International
Now considered one of the country's leading lighting experts, Sally spends much of her time travelling all over the world to design lighting schemes for individual and corporate clients. Sally has written three very successful, well-received books on the subject of lighting.
www.johncullenlighting.co.uk

Luke Thomas
Senior Lighting Designer,
John Cullen Lighting
Luke developed his passion for lighting whilst studying Product Design and Innovation, After graduating with a first class honours degree, Luke spent a short time as a freelance designer before joining John Cullen in 2008.
www.johncullenlighting.co.uk

Sue Timney
President, BIID
Sue Timney is an influential interior designer that has worked in Britain, Europe and Japan for over 30 years creating interior projects that celebrate her own brand of exotic classicism under the Timney Fowler banner. She is the President of the British Institute of Interior Design and an Honorary Fellow of the Royal College of Art.
www.suetimney.com

Asifa Tirmizi
Principal, Tirmizi Campbell
Asifa has a Master of Architecture Degree and a Master of Science in Real Estate Development degree. She also has experience of working on corporate interiors, exhibit design and residential renovation projects.
www.tirmizicampbell.com

Rebecca Tucker and Helen
Fewster, Suna Interior Design
Suna Interior Design is a boutique interior design consultancy with a unique style and vast knowledge of creating polished, bespoke designs.
www.sunainteriordesign.com

Sarah Ward
Founder, Sarah Ward
Associates Ltd
Sarah Ward Associates has completed a large number of prestigious commissions throughout the UK and Internationally. Sarah has served on the board of BIID.
www.sarahwardassociates.com

Ros Wilson
Founder,
Roselind Wilson Design
Ros started working in the industry in South Africa 12 years ago. Moving to London she worked in senior positions and gained valuable experience with notable designers David Collins and Helen Green.
www.sunainteriordesign.com

Above: *GR Residence in Prewar Building, New York City, designed by Tirmizi Campbell*
Photography by: *Hulya Kolabas*

INTERIOR DESIGN YEARBOOK 2013

Foreword: Sue Timney

President, British Institute of Interior Design

Travelling nomadically as a child from one country, school and house to another, made me sure that one day my own home was definitely going to be my castle, and I think this dictum applies to most of us. We cherish our homes, we are proud of them; they are a positive way of expressing ourselves.

The sheer quantity of self-help interior programmes on television is testament to these feelings. We love these shows, and, of course, sometimes love to hate them too! Why? Because, what they sometimes do is cheapen the value of design and expertise required to raise actual standards of skills, knowledge and professionalism in our very visual world.

Good interior design is not just about these qualities though – it's also about the magic called creativity. In essence good interior design is a language that brings everything together - creativity, skills, knowledge and professionalism,

and like all languages it can be learnt with the right support.

As President of The British Institute of interior Design I know only too well that if we don't promote a good design ethic in this country then this design 'language' will be lost to future generations and standards will slip.

That is why the Institute, as the pre-eminent body, representing interior designers in this country – is set to raise standards throughout the interior design community in 2013. We, the BIID are launching a Professional Pathway in 2013, which means, ultimately, that all our Designer Members will have reached our high standards. This Institute standard will take on average four years of design experience after graduation to reach. Yes, we are indeed raising the bar. The beneficiary of such a mission being you, the public.

In essence, the result will be that when you see the BIID membership signage you can be

assured that the interior designer you employ has reached our standards in design process, practice and regulation. Through this assurance of quality we aim to demystify the process of appointing a designer and ensure that as a client - you have a professional and experienced designer working with and supporting you.

This latest edition of the Yearbook or "little black book" as I like to call it is an essential guide and gallery of some of the country's most respected and influential designers and their work. There is information and advice on colour and products and it offers a wealth of supportive advice that you can refer to whether your projects are large or small. It is a showcase for new and existing talent and an amazing resource for established product and service companies... all essential ingredients within. In fact, it's part of the magic ingredient behind a very successful interior design.

Photo Casebook

The scale and style of work presented in this edition of the photo casebook is nothing short of exquisite. The designers featured in this section have opened up their portfolios and allowed us to take inspiration from their outstanding work. Whether it is a private residence, a luxury estate or a wonder of a hotel, there are palettes, furnishings, lighting fixtures and design concepts for every interior. Take note as we guide you through home after home of impeccable personal style and also take time to reflect on the prevalence and importance of commercial design and how it affects trends in home design. From a chalet nestled atop the French mountains to a condo in Miami or a Thames riverside penthouse, the photo casebook has savoured every essence of design to bring you a collection of incredible spaces to inform your design decisions over the coming year.

BATHED IN LIGHT

Anna Dodonova was given the brief to create a contemporary family apartment located in a new building development in Knightsbridge, London. Faced with a brief of changing the interior layout and making the space feel as spacious, Anna changed the apartment layout by completely opening the entrance area and installing a walk in wardrobe and guest bathroom. There is now an open-plan living and dining room space with breathtaking views of London. The 300 square metres property is bathed in light and bright shades of white and ivory, blending contemporary design with timeless glamour. With the clever use of lighting and mirrors, Anna created the illusion of higher ceilings and larger rooms. The apartment is filled with bright energy and a flow of light from room to room. The white and ivory colour palette is complemented by the use of accent colour accessories. Anna used shiny lacquered finishes on some of the surfaces and the best quality fabrics and leathers. From sand touch wallpaper and glass beads to fine studded curtains, the different textures featured throughout the apartment gives all the spaces depth and character.

Lancelot Place, Knightsbridge, London was designed by Anna Dodonova, Anna Casa Interiors and completed in July 2012. Photography by Mel Yates.

TAILORED LIVING IN LONDON

The Grosvenor House Apartments by Jumeirah Living is actually a new hotel concept on Park Lane, London. Located in the iconic Lutyens building dating from the 1920s. Grosvenor House Apartments include four spacious and luxurious single strata penthouses on the top floor. Anouska Hempel acted as a design consultant for the stylish interiors, which combines classic British design with dark oak timber flooring and more contemporary touches, including tailored wall panelling, oversized stone bathrooms, Dartington glassware and Royal Doulton china. Most furniture on the project is bespoke designed by Anouska Hempel and architects Woods Bagot, including the sofas and dining room tables. The penthouse apartments include state-of-the-art bespoke designed Poggenpohl kitchens and Carrera Marble bathrooms.

Grosvenor House apartments, Jumeirah Living, London was designed by Anouska Hempel and Woods Bagot and completed in February 2012.

AN ART COLLECTORS DREAM

April Russell Designs was commissioned to carry out the renovation and interior design of this stunning mansion house in the heart of Belgravia. The brief was to contemporise yet retain the original listed regency features and also to provide an appropriate backdrop that would enhance the client's extensive collection of modern artwork and sculpture. Special attention was paid to lighting and paint finishes including textured walls and unique effects such as bespoke crackled glazed panels to add a different dimension. The kitchen and dining area had innovative quartz surfaces and metal finishes for a striking and unique finish. A specialist painter used pearlescent techniques on the walls so that the light bounced off the walls. In the cinema room the walls were covered in fabric to give a textured finish as well as sound-proofing. Many items of furniture were sourced from post war Italy and the remaining items were custom designed by April Russell Designs.

Belgravia, London was designed by April Russell Designs and completed in April 2012. Photography by Luke Foreman.

CAMBRIDGE CONSERVATION

This fine Grade II listed property is in a conservation area of
Cambridge. Not touched for over 30 years the house has been
completely renovated and refurbished and now boasts four
bedrooms, two bathrooms, two reception rooms and a large open
plan kitchen diner and living space on the lower ground floor. The
latter space required the removal of five internal walls and tonnes
of clay to lower the floor by half a metre to create the space. The
classic contemporary scheme complements the architecture of
the house and interiors but with some surprise elements.

*The Cambridge Villa, Cambridge was designed by Hugh Jamieson
of At Home Interior Design Consultants and was completed in
August 2012. Photography by Richard Gooding.*

CHALET IN THE SUN

Perched at the top of the mountain above Villars, this stunning chalet, designed by Sir Norman Foster, commands views of the entire valley below. The brief for Mark Howorth was to create an interior that oozed relaxation and style, the premise being that after a hard days skiing one wants comfort and a space to chill-out in. Large-scale furnishings and innovative lighting make this space feel cosy even though the main living space soars three storeys high. The 4m high custom chandelier above the dining table is formed of 600 weathered copper squares which reflect the mountain light over all the walls and the main atrium. The feature fireplace adds show stopping wow factor as it was designed with a huge glazed panel that looked on to the large terrace so the fireplace can be enjoyed from the outside. Due to this design you can see this fireplace from the village.

Chalet Solais, Villars, France was designed by Mark Howorth of Callender Howorth and completed in April 2012. Photography by Michael Elkan.

MARYLEBONE OR MIAMI

This mews house, tucked away in the heart of Marylebone, really could be in Miami. From the outside the property looks like a typical stylish modernised London mews house, but once you step inside the whole place comes alive. There are three main levels; ground floor, lower ground floor and first floor. The brief from the bachelor client was to create a place with a wow factor which was also somewhere that he could entertain his friends. The abundance of glass used throughout allows light to flood the house making it feel bright and airy. All of the windows at the rear of the house fully open to a marble courtyard complete with three-storey water feature. The sleek finishes and custom furniture add to a real level of luxury and style making this bachelor pad somewhere the owner can really enjoy hanging out. Mark spent a lot of time in galleries with the client to help him to amass an impressive art collection.

Marylebone Mews House, London was designed by Mark Howorth of Callender Howorth and was completed in May 2012.
Photography by Darren Cheung.

HARMONY AND ELEGANCE

Christine May was originally contacted by the owners of this six-bedroom property to redesign the kitchen/diner. After successfully completing this project Christine was asked to work on other rooms throughout the house one at a time to suit the clients budget. The brief was to create a luxurious but understated space that would be a quiet refuge in the months and years to come. The bedroom suite leads off the main landing and comprises an inner hallway with the bathroom first on the right; next, an open arch leads into the semi open plan bedroom area while further at the end of the inner hallway are the dressing rooms. The finished master suite is harmonious and elegant.

Hadley Wood family residence, Hertfordshire was designed by Christine May of Christine May Interiors and completed in July 2012. Photography by Richard Gooding.

MID-CENTURY MODERNITY

Clare Pascoe has cleverly combined her flare for Mid-Century furniture craft with a thoroughly modern home to create a very clean palette for living. Mixing restored pieces of Mid-Century furniture with an architectural property that really took in the beautiful landscape, this project succeeds on many levels, delivering a space for a family to enjoy, whilst combining their passion for art.

The Coach House, Berkshire, England was designed by Clare Pascoe, Pascoe Interiors Ltd, completed in 2012.

A MID-CENTURY CELEBRATION

Pascoe Interiors were brought in by the new owners to furnish, decorate and style the interiors of this Spitalfields home. The house was designed as a two-bedroom home, with the option of a third suite / home office space in the basement. To add humour to the design of the space, Clare accessorised each room with tremendous style and individuality for example using a mannequin lamp by Jimmie Martin in the salon and using vintage ladders as shelf storage for the owner's books and ornaments in the sitting room. The overall feel of this property is a contemporary celebration of Mid Century furniture, demonstrating how Pascoe Interiors' signature Vintage Contemporary style delivers an eclectic mix across the mid-century era, off set with contemporary elements. The result in a timeless interior that is not slavishly vintage, but that discretely showcases a wealth of highly collectable original furniture and artwork.

Spitalfields, London was designed by Clare Pascoe of Pascoe and completed in June 2012. Photography by Alex James.

ENGLISH ARCHITECTURE GREETS ITALIAN STYLE

Massimo is located in a distinguished landmark building that was once the site of the Metropole Hotel that first opened in 1886. The design draws inspiration from the late Victorian period of the building, mixing English architectural references with classical Italian styling, the design reflects both the beauty and simplicity of Massimo's cooking. With its high vaulted ceiling the overall space has a feeling of grandeur but is slightly softened through the addition of a shallow ceiling and graceful lunettes above each of the many windows. The overall mood of relaxed elegance is followed throughout using a refined colour palette of black, white and rich green.

Massimo, London, was designed by the David Collins Studio and completed in April 2011.

NY SOPHISTICATION WITH A COASTAL TOUCH

This gorgeous Miami private residence, a spacious 4,000 sq. ft., combines light, airy coastal touches with an edgy New York sophistication, due in part to objects d'art selected by GRADE, including numerous paintings by modern American artist Peter Tunney. The result is an eclectic, modern home for a family, characterised by unique mid-century influences - memorable and chic furniture and décor elements, providing the utmost in comfort and accessibility. The lighter palette complements the endless light the residence receives, with nods to the breezy Oceanside surroundings. With striking furniture pieces custom-designed by GRADE - a floating bench, floating desk and slide dining table among them, the space emphasises functionality and style, with thoughtful consideration to how the client's family interacts and spends time together.

The Miami Condo, Aventura, FL was designed by GRADE and completed in spring 2012.

REFLECTING THE CITY SURROUNDINGS

The Radisson Blu Aqua Hotel is located on the first 18 floors of the 81-storey Aqua Tower, Chicago, named "Skyscraper of the Year" by Emporis. Graven Images' Creative Director Jim Hamilton carefully handpicked features and materials reflective of the city of Chicago to implement a design relevant to the surroundings and everyday life. Steel work features heavily throughout the interiors, paying homage to the city's iconic skyscrapers. Similarly, the lobby's brick walls studded with backlit glass blocks resemble the cityscape seen from a distance. Representing the Radisson Blu brand and Chicago's unique architectural style, a thought-provoking, contemporary design crafted by Graven Images prevails throughout. The 20-ton steel staircase leading to the mosaic-tiled Filini Restaurant, a dramatic Egyptian brass medallion screen wall and a 50-foot-long gas fireplace are some of the most distinctive elements.

Radisson Blu Aqua Hotel, Chicago was designed by Graven Images and completed in November 2011.

GEORGIAN ESTATE, SECRET ESCAPE

This converted outbuilding used to form part of a Georgian estate and is located in a beautifully landscaped park. Although the ground floor flowed well, the upstairs was poorly designed and needed reconfiguring to create a spacious master bedroom, dressing room and bathroom suite. The brief from the client was to create a timeless comfortable interior that flows throughout but incorporating more luxurious living spaces and modern conveniences. The previous owners had retained the false ceiling, which made the rooms gloomy. Pam Cox created the wow factor for the en-suite open plan master bath by adding a sunken bath into a platform beneath the eaves, so at night you can lie in the tub and gaze through the skylight at the stars. While the bathroom has an on-trend look, the bedroom is more rustic in style. The exposed beans were whitewashed, and the panelling painted in a similar fashion creating a timeless comfortable interior not only in the bedroom, but throughout the home.

Henley Park Coach House, Henley, Oxfordshire was designed by Pam Cox of Ham Interiors and completed in December 2011. Photography by Robert Sanderson.

A WORLDLY COLLECTION

Once a collection of separate buildings, the Walled Garden property now flows effortlessly together with style and panache. Situated close to the River Thames on the borders of Buckinghamshire and Oxfordshire, this unique family home is cleverly disguised behind a collection of traditional black barn exteriors and an 11ft high flint wall. Although the house and its outbuildings needed a lot of work, it was still perfect for its new owners, Pam and Nick Cox. Converting properties is what they have done pretty much all their working lives so they saw it as an opportunity to adapt things to suit their family's needs. Gradually over seven years the property has been completely remodelled internally whilst retaining all the character of the original exterior. The former apple store is now self-contained with three bedrooms, two bathrooms and a sitting room. The interior throughout is an eclectic but elegant and timeless mix of styles and textures with many antique pieces dotted around which have been collected on Nick and Pam's travels.

Walled Garden, Henley, Oxfordshire was designed by Pam Cox of Ham Interiors and completed in February 2012. Photography by Alex James.

HARK BACK TO GLAMOUR

The Gallery at HBA London was commissioned to restore and reinvent the public areas and guestrooms of the legendary Hotel Maria Cristina. The design celebrates the style and sensuality of the female stars of stage and screen that have stayed and played there. The spirit of this Luxury Collection hotel has been rekindled to evoke the glamour, opulence and celebrity that belong to it. Fluid Art Nouveau detailing forms an exquisite canvas for HBA's luxurious and comfortable design. Hues of lavender adorn some of the rooms and others are styled in shades of sky blue, while chocolate tones enrich the suites. The lobby has been extended and softened and adjacent corridors have intimate seating areas nestled next to immense arched doorways. Pale coffee-toned velvets, the softest ecru leather lounge chairs, and cerise accents in the abstract damask second entrance area now has the intimate feel of a residential library.

Hotel Maria Cristina, San Sebastian, Spain was designed by The Gallery at HBA London and completed in July 2012. Photography by Starwood Hotels & Resorts.

FASHION'S INFLUENCE

The newly renamed Couture Suite at The St. Regis Rome draws inspiration from the St. Regis "passion points" of fashion, art and literature, as well as the city's renowned design studios. Its signature furnishings and accessories celebrate the best of Italian style. In particular, the designers' muse was the couturier Valentino. With their timeless grace, emphasis upon flowing shapes and meticulous attention to detail, the essence of his creations has been woven into the rooms' design. The master bedroom features an elegant central living room where details unfold layer by layer. A high ceiling and neutral, linen-textured walls form the backdrop for its exquisitely luxurious materials and intricate embellishments, such as the nail-head trim on the timber panelling and millwork, the softest Italian leathers and finely stitched embroidery. A grand antiqued mirror above the fireplace reflects the light from the cascading glass rods of the shimmering chandelier. The three bedrooms evoke the glamour and display of the fashion catwalk.

Couture Suite, St Regis Hotel, Rome was designed by The Gallery at HBA London and completed in July 2012. Photography by Eric Laignel.

BY ROYAL APPOINTMENT

Inspired by Queen Elizabeth II, The Gallery has created a suite modelled in part on Her Majesty's acclaimed fashion sense. References to royalty are subtle as The Gallery's intention has been to create a home, which will be comfortable for dignitaries from all corners of the world. The result blends Art Deco touches with a contemporary interpretation of the opulent finishes found in royal palaces. Reflective surfaces creatively woven into the interiors increase its sense of spaciousness and luminosity. In the living room, antiqued mirrors border the coved ceiling to create an illusion of height, the coffee and side tables have glazed finishes, and a tufted leather bench is supported by a mirrored base.

InterContinental Park Lane Royal Suite, London was designed by The Gallery at HBA London studio and completed in October 2012. Photography by Will Pryce.

BEAUTIFUL SUN ROOM

Helen's brief was to create a comfortable home for a family requiring a relaxed space to suit their busy lifestyle. The focus was on creating a home that looked good, but had a lived-in and comfortable feel. Using a neutral, but warm, colour palette, Helen has focused on a relaxed feel, with open fires, lots of texture and distressed leather sofas. A large farmhouse kitchen sits at the centre of the home, but a beautiful sun room opening on to the gardens provides a great entertaining space, and a home office set away from the kitchen ensures work and play spaces are kept separate.

This family home in Kerry, Republic of Ireland was designed by Helen Turkington and completed in 2011. Photography by Barry Murphy.

ON THE RIVERSIDE

Kew Bridge is a development of luxury apartments and penthouses on London's riverside, set around a public piazza, and making the most of the spectacular location on the Thames. The apartment has a classic, contemporary and timeless appeal. Helen made the most of the huge amount of natural light and open plan design by using a neutral palette of stone, ice blue and dove grey. She created interest with texture, pieces of dark wood furniture and subtle lighting.

Penthouse Apartment, Kew Bridge was designed by Helen Turkington and completed in April 2012.
Photography by Patrick Steele.

MODERN BAROQUE ELEGANCE

JOI-Design aimed to preserve the unique character of the original estate, while also creating a stylish spa destination that would attract new tourists to Clervaux, a picturesque medieval village located in the Clerve valley of northern Luxembourg. The concept for the interior décor blends stylised Baroque elements with contemporary twists, creating a relaxed yet sophisticated ambience. Guests are introduced to this 'Modern Baroque' elegance from the moment they enter the hotel: plush red carpeting forms a runway atop the ebony polished granite floors, the walls are lined with a silver and grey damask patterned covering, and an ornately scrolled black chandelier sparkles above.

Le Clervaux Boutique & Design Hotel, Luxembourg was designed by JOI-Design GmbH, Hamburg and completed in September 2012. Photography by JOI-Design GmbH.

SOUTH AFRICAN HERITAGE IN CANARY WHARF

The brief for this penthouse project was to create the perfect pied-à-terre for entertaining international clients and relaxing away from the family. Lawson Robb were asked to incorporate an essence of the client's Sri Lankan heritage with the use of symbolic iconography and a sumptuous palette. A stunning bespoke bar was the main focal point of the living room. Incorporating both style, with antique decanter pendants, this has proven to be the perfect backdrop for parties. The latest integrated audio visual technology was also incorporated with flexible lighting to enhance the required ambience of any occasion. A thread of opulence runs through the apartment with the use of glistening gold wallpaper throughout the lobby, down the spiral staircase and along the lower floor hallways. A two tier Murano glass chandelier, infused with gold dust delicately hangs in the main entrance lobby adding to this sense of extravagance that the client was keen to achieve.

Penthouse Apartment, Canary Wharf, London was designed by Lawson Robb and completed in April 2012.

ECLECTIC APARTMENT DESIGN

Lawson Robb were asked to create an apartment for the ultra and high net worth market with a classic/modern approach. It was important that the style complemented the stunning Georgian features and architectural heritage of the property, so a scheme that was not too elaborate but not plain, impressive but not ostentatious, classic yet relevant to modern living and elegant with longevity was created. Inspiration for the concept was drawn from elements of certain cultural styles: the rich intricate inlays of the Middle East; the vibrancy of Southern Asia, American understated classical detailing paired with the simple lines and impeccable quality of European design. Influences were also taken from the calm proportions and structured patterns of the Far East and the opulent detailing seen in traditional Russian style.

The Lancasters Hyde Park, London, was designed by Alexia Osborne, Lawson Robb and completed in July 2011. Photography by Tom Sullam.

INTERNATIONAL DESIGN

This imposing villa in Kuwait, was designed for a private client by leading interior designer, Louise Bradley. The brief was to create a truly spectacular family home, that was also practical and comfortable - somewhere that would work both as a modern luxury villa for entertaining, but also as a family home with functional living spaces. Louise had to inject glamour and sophistication into the vast space, whilst creating different areas within the open plan format. Using a combination of pared-down, contemporary design with some extravagant statement pieces, the villa retains a spacious and relaxed atmosphere without losing any of its 'wow factor'. Every item was created to the highest specification, with bespoke pieces of furniture designed for the property and specialist finishes used throughout. The property includes an internal courtyard with a private swimming pool. Beautifully lit at night, the courtyard provides a stunning focal point for the whole villa.

Family Villa, Kuwait, was designed by Louise Bradley and completed in November 2011. Photography by Ray Main.

BRINGING LONDON TO LEEDS

Lucia was asked to bring the opulence and sophistication of the owners' Knightsbridge apartment to a substantial new build house in Harrogate. The real challenge was to bring the same level of theatre, excitement and finish to an expansive, and relatively featureless, new build house in North Yorkshire. The main drawing room exploits contrasts between materials and textures to create this opulent space. By hiding the TV behind two-way mirror it gives this room more flexibility to either use as an informal or more formal drawing room. The existing master suite was enlarged, engulfing two of the secondary bedrooms, to incorporate a walk in dressing room that opens into a large sitting room and large bathroom suite, all finished with the finest of materials. An eaved loft room was chosen to be the location for a bespoke cinema. The awkward roof angles were replaced with the elegant tapering lines of a clamshell ceiling reminiscent of a more decadent era.

Belgrave House, Harrogate was designed by Lucia Caballero at Caballero Interior Design and completed in February 2012. Photography by Andrew Beasley Photography.

ALPINE ATMOSPHERE

With its abundance of space, stylish décor and furnishings and every creature comfort imaginable, this redesigned ski chalet is the ultimate alpine retreat. The design brief for this particular residence was "to create something comfortable, somewhere that was a good entertaining space and that had a sort of Ralph Lauren feel to it – a real home away from home". The emphasis has to be on warmth, comfort and discreet yet discernible luxury. Furnishings and accessories, which were either bespoke or sourced throughout Europe, include a pair of Italian, high-backed, over-sized sofas, Swedish light fittings and French table lamps with silk shades.

Courchevel chalet, Courchevel, France was designed by Nico Yiannikkou of Y2DC and completed in April 2012. Photography by Barry Murphy.

PRACTICAL LIVING

Honey Tye House was a new build farm house project. Planning permission was granted and secured by the digging and pouring of the foundations in the 1970's and the project then ceased. Lindsey Rendall worked with the original footprint of the property to re-design both the interior and exterior to suit today's living style and the location now being an area of 'outstanding national beauty'. The essential aim was to create a practical family home with good storage, good green credentials, a versatile open plan living space and design longevity.

Honey Tye House was designed by Rendall & Wright and completed in summer 2011.

BACK TO NATURE

Lindsay was tasked with converting an old Suffolk dairy and adjoining cow stables into a chic, contemporary living space, maintaining a homely interior, which would highlight the wealth of beautiful original features of the listed building. Contemporary shapes and clean lines were used as well as harder shapes, which were softened by an array of natural fabrics, including wool, linens and silk. Glass was used as a regular feature as it extenuated the serene atmosphere and feeling of spaciousness. Lindsey commissioned furniture made and supplied by local Suffolk craftsmen. A sense of provenance was brought to the design, with local artist's work being displayed throughout the property. Curvaceous shapes in the bathroom instantly added a relaxing flow of movement and a touch of elegance.

Sparrows Nest Farm dairy conversion, Suffolk, was designed by Lindsey Rendall of Rendall & Wright for a private client and completed in October 2011. Photography by Craig Girling.

SHOW-STOPPING 17TH CENTURY FARMHOUSE

At the end of a sweeping driveway, set in nine acres of stunning, rolling grounds, lies a fine grade II listed 17th century farmhouse. Having been owned by the same family for almost half a century, the property had an established presence with elegant living spaces, but the new owners were looking to bring this historic property up to date to create a family home both modern and classical which retained the period features, with practicality and comfort a priority. Lindsey created an elegant atmosphere and feeling of space in the once gloomy dining room by French polishing and introducing antiqued mirrored sections within the original wooden panelling. Vivid red studded leather and velvet dining chairs added a splash of glamour to the room. For the main reception room, Lindsey designed a lighter, more feminine space using soft grey hues, inky blue shades. A punch of rich red in the reception room created harmony between the two adjoining spaces. Tactile fabrics were a central theme in the design as the materials added a sense of warmth and luxury. A show-stopping deep-buttoned storage ottoman takes centre stage in this elegant room.

17th Century Farmhouse, Surrey was designed by Lindsey Rendall of Rendall & Wright and completed in December 2011. Photography by Craig Girling.

RIVERSIDE RESPLENDENCE

Roland's inspiration for the colours, finishes, textures for both the hard finishes and soft furnishings for this project, came from the flowers, plants, leaves and beautiful summer landscape in Sweden. His main intention was to maximise light so skylights were introduced wherever possible including in the entrance hall, stairwell and all bathrooms. The client requested that the master bedroom exuded glamour but which was still as comfortable and had all the mod cons of a luxury five Star Hotel. The open plan living area consists of a piano area and bar, kitchen and dining, cloakroom and wow factor guest wc. It is completely open plan living, working and entertaining space with no visible columns encroaching into the space. Contemporary timber panelling on the rear walls to anchor the space and conceal the kitchen equipment and storage. The window walls painted with lambrequins to house hand woven sustainable natural fibre roman blinds. The overall impression of the space is warm, relaxed and comfortable but still very chic.

The riverside duplex penthouse, London, was designed by Roland Hartmann of Hartmann Designs and completed in April 2012. Photography by Richard Gooding.

TIMELESS MODERNITY

Cornwall House is a new build multi storey residential apartment building situated close to Regents Park, London. Working alongside the architects, Roselind Wilson Design was appointed to design the interior space of the apartment to portray a sense of luxury and affluent living to a tight budget and installation deadline. The interior design scheme comprised of a soft neutral palette of creams and beige, offset by dark chocolate timbers and accents of blue and gold in the open plan living space. The remainder of the apartment continues along the line of the soft palette with an accent of gold throughout. The palette and proportions of the furniture were all carefully considered so as not to be overbearing. The scheme enhances the features and creates a space, which is modern yet timeless.

Cornwall House, London was designed by Roselind Wilson of Roselind Wilson Design and completed in September 2012. Photography by Richard Warte.

TOWN HOUSE ON THE THAMES

Here, a fresh, clean, contemporary "London" look has been created. Structurally, the main alterations were in the entrance hall; SWA widened the main doors from the hall to the sitting room to allow maximum light and symmetry. This provided a clear view straight through to the garden, thereby enhancing the space. Sarah and her team used a neutral palette in the main space, commissioning bespoke art to add vibrancy and colour. A central crystal chandelier in the sitting room is visible throughout the ground floor. The chandelier very much works like moving art, owing to the way both the natural and artificial light works its magic on the crystal at different times of day. The bathrooms are modern with state of the art equipment. The four bedrooms all have a unique feel to provide interesting spaces. The technology and lighting are right up to date using LED's balanced with directional halogens to add variety and impact.

Riverside, Marlow, Buckinghamshire was designed by Sarah Ward of Sarah Ward Associates Ltd and completed in April 2012. Photography by Ollie Weait.

BELGRAVIA BEAUTY

Belgraves London, set in the heart of Belgravia is the internationally-renowned Thompson Hotels' London Flagship Hotel. Tara Bernerd & Partners were responsible for the full interior architecture and design of this 85 bedroom hotel, lounge lobby, bars and restaurant. The design brief was to keep the Thompson look, but bring it to Belgravia and not limit the demographic of guests. Tara and her team reintroduced sandblasted brick walls and grey oak flooring, which contrasted with the leather and bronze clad columns and an eclectic mix of contemporary and vintage furniture pieces giving an inviting clubby feel to the space.

Belgraves, London was designed by Tara Bernerd & Partners and completed in February 2012. Photography by Philip Vile.

THE HEART OF HONG KONG

Tara Bernerd & Partners were appointed to design a Penthouse at the iconic, award winning HighCliff. Situated at The Peak, in the heart of the city, HighCliff is the tallest residential tower in Hong Kong. Penthouse 68 occupies the entire floor-plate of the 68th floor. This super-deluxe, 3,500 sq ft apartment has remarkable 360 degree views of the city. The open plan living space is broken into distinct zones, each with its own special mood and raison d'être. Key consideration was given to intelligent living in terms of space planning. Detail in terms of joinery and feature walls was original and hand crafted. Textures throughout are earthy, warm and luxurious with stained oak, bronze and a combination of sandstone and timber flooring, yet used with a modern, edgy approach. Colours are natural and muted, but with sudden contrasts to reflect the mood.

Penthouse 68, HighCliff, Central Hong Kong was designed by Tara Bernerd and Partners and completed in October 2011. Photography by Philip Vile.

SCHOOL HOUSE TURNED ART HOUSE

A former school, this four bedroom apartment has previously proved difficult to sell due to the large amount of 'wasted space' that was taken up by the staircase. The space was perfect however for one private art collector client to show off his amazing contemporary collection. Taylor Howes completely redesigned the space, including a new staircase with hand-blown glass balls by Anthony Stern and beautiful joinery throughout.

Academy Gardens, Kensington, London was designed by Gail Taylor, Sheila El Hadery, Sandra Drechsler and Julie Coutts at Taylor Howes Designs Ltd and completed in June 2011.

QUIRKY ACCENTS

A stylish classic contemporary apartment with quirky accents, this
four bedroom property was designed as a show flat, and sold for a
record sum before it was officially put on the market. Taylor Howes
not only furnished the apartment but changed the flooring,
created a stunning hallway and designed the living room joinery.

*Lowndes Square, Knightsbridge, London was designed by Karen
Howes, Sheila El Hadery, Sandra Drechsler and Julie Coutts at
Taylor Howes Designs Ltd and completed in December 2011.*

MAXIMUM MARBLE DESIGN

This 2800sqft apartment in Knightsbridge was designed for a property developer who was looking for a classic contemporary style. The Taylor Howes team carried out the build work, completely reconfiguring the space, remodelling all the bathrooms and designing a number of bespoke built in joinery pieces. Key pieces include the use of Carrara Marble in the Master Bathroom and kitchen and the halo lit mirror in the Master Bathroom.

This second Lowndes Square, Knightsbridge, London project was designed by Karen Howes Designs Ltd, Sandra Drechsler, Sheila El Hadery, Olivia Shaw and Julie Coutts at Taylor Howes and completed in February 2012.

EMPHASISING EXISTING ARCHITECTURE

This property is one of the finest and most elegant houses in South West London, where the traditional William and Mary architecture exists in harmony with the more recent contemporary design. Taylor Howes worked on this listed property closely with the clients to create a warm family home, mixing cutting edge contemporary design with existing period features to create a unique and stunning property. One of the main features was the contemporary glass extension at the back of the house creating an "indoor outdoor" feel and the swimming pool appeared to flow seamlessly through into the rill in the garden and down to a Lorenzo Quinn sculpture at the end of the vista.

This Richmond, Surrey home was designed by Julie Coutts, Gail Taylor, Jane Landino and Betty Bettinson at Taylor Howes Designs Ltd and completed in May 2011.

NEW YORK CLASSIC

The GR residence was a project in which two apartments were combined. The first challenge was to create one unified apartment. Tirmizi Campbell created three bedrooms and two full bathrooms along with a large kitchen and great room from the original separated spaces. This client wanted a more classic decorative look with some modern accents such as lighting and fixtures. Tirmizi Campbell refurbished the existing fireplace with new contemporary tiles and kept the decorative mantles, with decorative moldings and baseboards. The kitchen is contemporary with the clean thick stone and mixed colour use of white and dark wood cabinets. The cabinets themselves are modern with a slight recessed panel detail, which compliments the decorative moldings. Tirmizi Campbell decided to go with a bright punch of colour in the entry to contrast the neutral palette of the rest of the apartment.

GR Residence in Prewar Building, New York City was designed by Asifa Tirmizi and Scot Campbell at Tirmizi Campbell and completed in the late part of 2010. Photography by Hulya Kolabas.

Above: Flemings Hotel, Mayfair, designed by Suna Interior Design

Trend concepts

The designers included in this issue are experienced across the board in designing homes in their entirety but here they have taken the time to look at the details, shedding some light on ways to achieve the perfect look for your home, whether it be in a busy hub of the home space like the kitchen or somewhere more indulgent and serene such as the bedroom or bathroom, the designers share their love of design and just how to make the most beautiful space within your home.

Trend: Luxury design in the home

By Sarah Ward
Founder, **Sarah Ward Associates Ltd**

Sarah Ward runs a team of Interior Designers with over 20 years experience working at the highest level within the residential, new home and commercial sectors. Sarah has served on the board of BIID and has acted as judge and advisor at major exhibitions and events. Sarah Ward Associates have completed a large number of prestigious commissions throughout the UK and Internationally. Sarah is the resident Interiors Advice expert for Primelocation.com. Here Sarah talks about creating luxury in your home.

I believe that the power and apparent 'normality' of high end branding these days has become synonymous with luxury. Luxury brands span across many sectors from airlines, hotels, travel goods, clothing and footwear, foods and restaurants to name a few examples. Branding has increased awareness of luxury and made it more available. Consequently we have learnt to assume an expectation of a certain standard. Luxury in interior design is no different. We each have our own perception of acceptable quality and that is absolutely a personal opinion. There is much opportunity these days to source and acquire luxury goods at affordable prices.

Much as the high street fashion stores produce designer

Above: The decadent luxury of this room is all in the lighting and the positioning of the space

Above: *Sarah's designs have won her a coveted luxury award*

'look-a-like' clothing in a remarkably short space of time following fashion launches, equally the interior design industry produce 'faux-everything' to follow the top end product designers. The reality is that these days with advancing technology those 'copies' are good enough to grace all sorts of schemes.

To me luxury is ambience, often created by light albeit lamplight or candle light first and foremost. Then it is about opulence, which can be translated in terms of tactile fabrics and wall coverings. Thirdly, the use of generous scale of key furniture items exceeds expectation.

A definition of the word luxury is "the state of great comfort and extravagant living". Beauty is in the eye of the beholder, as the saying goes, but perceived 'luxury' is pretty consistent in terms of universal understanding and expectation.

In the marketing material for large new build houses the word 'luxury' generally appears in the text. We recently designed the interiors for a new build home by Octagon, which spanned 10,000 sq ft. It has won the Evening Standard's "Best New Luxury Home Award", thereby cementing the view that it is most definitely a luxury home.

A luxurious home should be elegant, comfortable, individual and should ooze aspiration and desire. The words glamour and opulence are also synonymous with luxury.

When thinking about how to achieve this level of luxury, it does not necessarily come attached with a huge price tag. There are some really excellent high street interior stores now. When we source a product we have a clear idea of what we are seeking, we take a very realistic approach always cross check these stores first to see what is available. Our job is to deliver the right project at the right value

and that means we need to take a practical approach. The ability to mix products of all levels effectively is where our experience comes in! The main difference is the 'feel' of the fabrics. There is nothing like the real thing but there are some handsome substitutes about.

Keeping the essence of a working home intact is a really important consideration in the design process. Having brought up four children and a few dogs in my time, together with being a house proud fiend, I managed to have a lot of hard floors softened by rugs. We always had a 'pale carpet and sofa room' in which the only house rules applied. So I picked my battles! I think to have the odd luxurious wall covering and plenty of mixed style tactile cushions about works well. They both add luxury and add a feel good factor and create a livable stylish home rather than a showpiece.

I find travelling a vital source

"To me luxury is ambience, often created by light albeit lamplight or candle light first and foremost."

Above: *Reflective surfaces and high-backed bespoke dining chairs*

of inspiration. When I travel I always look about as well as find time to settle down with a good book. New sights apart, travelling is also 'time out'. I tend to have extra clarity of thought which makes it an excellent time to absorb, adapt and then most likely place a version of what I have seen in a current project, or at least store it away for a rainy day. The interior design exhibitions are an obviously worth a visit as are main department stores. Ralph Lauren in Brompton Cross is full of wonderful expensive things. Albrissi at Sloane Square is a must.

I am an avid reader of the weekend supplements and always check out what's on to see if anything appeals. I like to visit new restaurants and I like to see the best hotels and just walk through the lobby areas.

It will be interesting to see what happens in 2013. In view of the continued current climate An achievable current look is to inject bursts of colour. This can be balanced by accessories such as cushions, art and candles These accessories are inexpensive to change for a fresh look. Colour adds warmth and interest. If added onto a blank canvas then we can have the best of both worlds!

www.sarahwardassociates.com

Above: *A leisure suite cellar designed by Sarah*

Trend: Furniture Design

By Anna Dodonova
Founder, **Anna Casa**

Bespoke interior designer Anna Dodonova is the founder of the pioneering Anna Casa design showroom, which exhibits exclusive, one-off pieces of luxury crafted furniture and lighting, scrupulously sourced from the world's brightest design stars and expert artisans. The Kiev-born businesswoman began following her interior design dream in 2003 when she left a flourishing graphic design career in her adopted home of Berlin to retrain in London. Drawing on her natural artistic flair and experience at the forefront of the German Capital's creative hub, Anna excelled in a range of interior design projects across London and Germany. She was soon able to set up her own business, Anna Casa Interiors, where she works on international projects for select residential and commercial clients from her base on the Chelsea waterfront. Anna's passion and expertise lies in the craft and creation of furniture and here she gives us her thoughtful insight into the seasonal approach to furniture design.

Being on top of the furniture trends is as much work as being up to date with the fashion world. Okay, we don't have four seasons on the furniture market, but we have two seasons in the interiors world.

Creating and introducing something new into our homes every six months is not quite the same as changing our winter and summer wardrobe. However, by attending homes shows like Saloni di Mobile in Milan in or Maison et Object in Paris, which are the most important exhibitions during the year, we get a sense of what's hot which means we can build on interior trends and mould our style.

In my new showroom in Mayfair, my aim is to show my clients what's trending in terms

Above: The Benao Dining table adds glamour and drama through textured and contrasting textiles

Above: *Anna's work in the Knightsbridge apartment floods the space with light by using tonal, paler palettes in the furniture pieces. Image by Mel Yates.*

Above: Key pieces of designer furniture really give rooms that edge, no matter how subtle it is. Image by Mel Yates.

of finishes, colours and style. Every four months I am changing the display and every six months I am bringing, directly from Italy, the latest must-have furniture pieces.

This year I started with lots of dark green and brown shades, mixing them with light taupes and warm beige colours. To me, it is important to create a balanced and comfortable atmosphere in your home, which is why I used these shades! In addition, I love to add drama and create a wow factor - as an example I would use a large crystal chandelier to make a room really glamorous and bring out all the colours featured in the room.

Next year I think we will be seeing furniture pieces in beige and blue tones - light blue and dark blue. Spaces will be elegantly hugged in high-end shiny fabrics and velvets and shiny lacquered furniture in dark brown wood finishes and ivory tones too. White furniture is also still a big trend, especially when

you mix it with bright colours like lime green or red! Grey tones, which I really love, will be mixed with powerful hues, like yellow or strong blue and pastel colours. You can design the full room in grey, its like the classic beige that we always use as a base for everything in the room and the house, you can't go wrong - just style all in light to dark shades of grey and add any of your favorite colourful accessories!

It may come as a surprise but gold is in, especially in more contemporary interiors! My advice to you is not to be afraid to mix in the metals, they are great, they reflect everything standing near them. Large mirrors will be seen more and more, they are prefect brighten up a room and make it look larger!

Having two interior seasons does not mean homes have to be changed twice a year, as I said before its not as easy to redesign a room as it is to buy a new dress! But, it is important to have a great piece of furniture in every

household and people should understand with some key you should spend on it for the quality. Having worked with Baxter for several years, I know that quality is a vital factor and I guarantee that for example a quality sofa from a company like Baxter will be a most comfortable, long lasting and eye catching piece in your living room. It's all about form and function.

www.annacasa.net

> ## "Creating and introducing something new into our homes every six months is not quite the same as changing our winter and summer wardrobe."

give yourself some

SPACE

www.livingstorage.co.uk

LA CORNUE

Where exceptional taste begins

Full hand-made kitchen by La Cornue

La Cornue, renowned for over a century as experts in range cooker design and manufacturing, unveil Domaine Culinaire, a new global architecture concept. Combining hobs, roasting ovens, refrigeration units and exclusive kitchen Cabinets.
Domaine Culinaire uses craftsman techniques to create an exceptional, made to measure kitchen.

a.table@la-cornue.com La Cornue

www.lacornue.com

Trend: Kitchens and Bathrooms

By Karen Howes
Co-Founder, **Taylor Howes Designs**

Karen is the driving force and inspiration behind Taylor Howes Designs, a company, which has carved a unique niche in the interior design market through an impeccable and comprehensive design service that the team offers to private clients and the commercial interior design industry. With a portfolio that includes plush apartments in the heart of London and second homes in the USA for private clients, the kitchen and bathrooms spaces of these homes requires understanding of a clients brief and appreciation of the way in which the spaces are used. Here, Karen discusses these two vital rooms and the way in which the spaces are evolving, causing a shift in expectations.

Getting to know you as a client and understanding the brief is crucial to the beginning process of a project, so really understanding how you are going to use the kitchen or bathroom space is important. The locations within the space obviously have a huge bearing and of course you need to always keep your practical hat on when designing a kitchen as well as making it look fabulous.

At Taylor Howes we ask clients a lot of questions. Do they do a lot of entertaining, do they want to eat in the kitchen, do they have a separate utility room, do they ever have staff in the kitchen? Then we go on to discuss the combination of finishes and textures in their kitchen – we have one client for

Above: *The kitchen is the hub of the home and is often chaotic with activity.*

Above: *Marble is once again prominent in bathrooms, heightening the sense of space and adding new depths of luxury.*

example who is having semi-precious stone worktops. It is very much a process about understanding whether practicality overrides the look or the other way round.

The majority of people allocate a lot of space to the kitchen as they understand in a normal family home it is the hub of the house and needs to include zones not just for cooking, but for sitting and watching TV and working, as well as providing great place to sit with the family and enjoy a great meal.

I think the look of kitchens over the past few years has generally become a lot lighter and more streamlined – it is not very often that someone wants a dark kitchen. The multi-functionality of a kitchen has been the big change and as there are so many demands on the space the planning of it needs a great deal of thought and consideration. When looking at up an coming trends, I think we are about to see a trend for slightly softer kitchens, the use of subway tiles – more colour coming into the space.

When considering the bathroom, it is often the most difficult room in a home to design and we always do a lot of detailed drawings and elevations to ensure that we can create the perfect glamorous bathroom. So again it is understanding you and your brief – do you like to shower or bathe, do you require two sinks, can we 'pinch' some more space from somewhere else to create the perfect 'his' and 'hers' spaces? All of these questions are integral to creating a clear picture before beginning on the design.

Marble is back in a big way in bathrooms – we are back to cladding all walls in book matched marbles. There are some amazing ways of treating stone with different textures to get a fresh new look. We have just commissioned a bronze panel to be made with a tree with blossom on that will sit behind a fabulous freestanding bath.

Of course practicality and hygiene are key but it needs to be glamorous as well which is why the use of marble and stone works so well. We are often working with tight spaces and we

need to get a great deal into that space as people are wanting separate showers to the baths, two basins and everything is getting bigger and bigger. So it is rather like a jigsaw puzzle to get the layout just right. Lighting is also key, so we often work with lighting designers to get the right levels of light depending on whether it is morning or evening.

We are now allocating more and more space to the bathroom. We have just finished a project in the States, which has a fireplace in it, a dressing table, armchair and circular stool. We have managed to keep the WC and shower slightly separate so it is a living space as well as a bathing space.

I think for the future we will continue to see bathrooms increasing in size as is already the case in many project briefs. At the top end you will see the use of semi-precious stones and fabulous bespoke mosaics being used. It's all about the injection of colour – bathrooms should be theatrical and indulgent.

www.taylorhowes.co.uk

oo stonearth

Natural & Unique

Imagine the feel of natural stone under your feet as you shower. Or running your hands along a travertine bath as you indulge in a little me-time. With Stonearth, you don't need to travel halfway across the globe to an exotic spa for a divine bathroom the way nature intended. You can have it in your own home.

Designing your very own solid wood and natural stone bathroom is effortless with Stonearth, from washstands and basins to mirrors and WC units – we've got it covered. For your free 180-pages brochure and design advice give us a call today.

T: 0115 714 8030   **F: 0115 872 0554**
E: info@stonearth.co.uk   www.stonearth.co.uk

Trend: Lighting

By the team at John Cullen Lighting

Sally Storey is Design Director of both John Cullen and Lighting Design International. Now considered one of the country's leading lighting experts, Sally heads up both teams and spends much of her time travelling all over the world to design lighting schemes for individual and corporate clients. Lucy Martin is works alongside Sally as Design Director of John Cullen Lighting heading up the award winning design team working on projects throughout the world. Alexandra Fry joined the lighting design team in 2002 and worked her way up to her current position of Associate. Sian started working for John Cullen in 2005 and is now a Senior Lighting Designer and Luke used to work as a freelance designer before joining the John Cullen team in 2008. Here, each designer shares their insight into the stunning world of successful lighting.

Sally Storey: Traditionally lighting was a single pendant in a room, nowadays, just as an interior designer layers with textures and materials, the lighting designer layers with light. This trend will certainly stand the test of time. There has gradually been a move towards more energy efficient solutions, which can now provide great alternatives to halogen and save you money on your energy bills. This will continue well beyond 2013 and enable us to reduce our energy consumption yet further without comprising on effect.

Lucy Martin: LED sources and the control of LED sources will also continue to occupy and perplex in equal measure in 2013. The speed at which it is

Above: Soft contour and strip lighting set within a wall or surface can soften the room and avoid the need for main lighting

A7725(4).7-2150 NI
↔ 2150 x 800 ↕ 80 cm   592 G9

FAUSTIG ¹⁹⁶⁰

Manufacturers of finest classical
and modern **Crystal Chandeliers**

KURT FAUSTIG KG
Kraillinger Straße 12
D-82131 Stockdorf / Munich
Germany

Tel.: +49 (0) 89 89 56 31 - 0
Fax: +49 (0) 89 89 56 31 - 72
email@faustig.de
www.faustig.de

43100-14 teak
ø 120 x 110 cm   14 E14

developing can make it very hard to get to grips with all its many permutations. It is however the future and 2013 will be marked by an improvement of the availability of good quality, more reasonably priced LED light sources and the availability of more refined control of the light source.

Sally Storey: When starting the lighting elements of a project, it is important to distinguish which types of lighting will be employed. Firstly one divides the lighting into two elements: decorative and architectural. The decorative sets the tone and is the visual reference selected by the interior designer but set by the lighting designer. The architectural lighting is the discreet effects that create the magic and often are the main illumination in any room. They can be divided into ambient, task and feature lighting. The ambient lighting is the general lighting in the room, which could be recessed downlights or wall washers or uplights. The next is the task lighting, which could be a wonderful desk light or work top lighting in a kitchen. Then there is feature lighting, which could be narrow beam lighting to arches, the focus on the centre of the dining table, picture lighting or lighting to shelves.

Lucy Martin: With reflected light you can make even the smallest room feel bigger. Decide what you want to light in a room and use directional fittings to create focal points. This is more effective than planting a tidy grid of spots in the ceiling which will only light the floor. Light from a directional spot will bounce off the lit object (wall, art, object etc) to provide reflected light. As your eye is always drawn to the brightest point, this will enhance a sense of space. Other good examples of how to extend space are to light under the stairs to include this area within the room or uplighting a window box or entire garden so that the eye does not stop at the window but goes beyond.

Sally Storey: Lighting is hard to visualise which is why we designed the John Cullen showroom to be a presentation of light so that everyone can understand the impact of light on a space. To make the best of any lighting scheme, it is ideal that you know the furniture layout prior to planning. Sometimes this can be difficult to visualise, which is why I often end up doing furniture layouts for them prior to planning the lighting.

Lucy Martin: My advice to anyone who is about to invest in the lighting of their home is to 'plan, test, invest and get some help'. Lighting is integral to any infrastructure. It has the power to have major impact and it is absolutely necessary to plan as early as you have an idea of structure. The advent of LED and the speed of its development necessitates actually seeing the light source itself. Don't just take someone's word for it. Good lighting does not come cheap. It is worth investing in the best you can afford. Get the best expert advice you can. A lighting designer is as imperative as an architect these days if you really want to get it right and save money both in energy terms and the number of fittings that you need to buy.

Lighting by room

Bathroom
Alex Fry: The key to successful bathroom lighting is being able to cater for different uses at different

Above: *Energy efficient bathroom lighting by John Cullen*

Above: 4. Energy efficiency in the hall and stairs can be created in conjunction with dramatic and inviting lighting

times of the day. Good face lighting is essential, achieved by using a combination of side lights and overhead lights for a shadow free effect. Using downlights in the shower or bath so that they skim lighting down tiles is preferable to a single downlight in the centre and reduces harsh glare. This can also be achieved by an architectural slot to hide fittings for a minimal effect. Allowing for a low level lighting circuit using miniature Cazalla LEDs is good for mood and can be linked to a motion sensor, great for family living where lights get left on. Ensuring all circuits are on dimmers gives maximum flexibility for a bright morning shower to a relaxed setting in the evenings.

Kitchen
Sian Parsons: Whatever the shape of the room, you need to consider the activities that are going to take place and find lighting solutions for each, ie cooking, dining and even, if a large open plan areas, children's homework and relaxing. Exposed light fittings collect the grime which cooking creates; if possible therefore, always opt for recessed or semi-recessed fittings. Under cupboard lighting is essential for lighting work surfaces and the new LED Eyelid Under Cupboard Lights or the LED Streamer strip light are excellent for both light output and saving energy. Always highlight the centre of an island where good task lighting is required. This can be achieved with pendants for a visual focus and combined with recessed LED Polestar downlights for a task light so you can see to work by. Think of layering lighting and add low level lights such as the 1w Cazalla into your kick plinths to wash light across the floor. Think carefully about controls; a pre-set scene system is ideal to create the right mood throughout the day.

Bedroom
Luke Thomas: The lighting in the bedroom needs to create a sense of relaxation and grid of downlights will work to your disadvantage. To create a soft atmospheric light, combine the use of table lamps, wall lights and pendants with reflected light from directional downlights. The downlights can be used to bounce light off wardrobe doors, artwork or window treatment to make the space feel more expansive. For excitement and drama, use recessed uplights, such as the 1w Lucca, set into the floor to light shutter boxes, window recesses or fireplaces. Those who are early to bed are often left irritated by the late night reading habits of their partners. To avoid confrontation, LED Cama bedside reading lights can be used for a focus spot onto the book without any spill of light to disturb sleepers. Combine this with two-way switching at the bedside and you won't have to leave your bed to turn off the lights when you go to sleep.

Main living space

Alex Fry: Main living spaces now come in such a variety of shapes, sizes and functions that the lighting needs to be flexible. Knowing the furniture layout early on will help in achieving the best lighting scheme. Having multiple circuits gives the flexibility to only light certain areas of large living spaces so that not everything is lit. Five amp circuits are essential for plug in solutions and these should correlate with the furniture so they are in convenient locations. Downlights should be positioned to accent features in the room and not over the seating area. Joinery offers a wealth of opportunity for interesting lighting solutions and if you don't know exactly what it will look like at the start, leave a supply so that it can be added in later. Scene setting control is an effective way of managing several circuits ensuring the best lighting scenario at all times.

Hallways/reception areas

Sian Parsons: It is the first experience one has of a house providing the all important first impression so essential to get right. The same rules apply as to any room such as the importance of dimming as you do not want to walk from a bright hallway into a dimmed, warm living sapce. Layering of light, for example, low level skirting lights can help by creating drama when linked with a focus at the end of a corridor. Alternatively it could be a combination of recessed downlights wall-washing the hall to make it more spacious used in conjunction with decorative wall lights or an over-size pendant that give the appearance of creating the light. Consider lighting something in the distance, ie on a half landing to increase the sense of space by drawing the eye through.

Outdoors

Luke Thomas: The main reason for lighting the exterior will be to extend your living space. Although you may never actually be in the garden after dark, lighting something outside will draw your eyes beyond the reflective glass of your windows and doors and create a more spacious feel. Rather than putting in a certain number of fittings per square metre for a flood light effect, concentrate on highlighting the main features of the garden which could include; trees, statues, external wall finishes, planting and water features. Often, less is more, but try not to position the lighting too sparsely as this will create a disjointed effect. Spiked spot lights, such as our new 1w Kew, offer the most flexibility, giving the option for lighting to be adjusted as the planting grows or changes from season to season. In this energy conscious society we should be considerate of using too much energy in an area that isn't directly occupied so LED fittings should be used where possible. These will also offer smaller and more discreet lighting solutions. We are now lighting town gardens with less than 60ws of energy!

www.johncullenlighting.co.uk

Above: *Take inspiration from magnificent spaces like the spa corridor at ESPA Life at Corinthia*

www.within4walls.co.uk
AWARD-WINNING LIGHTING AND INTERIORS

Trend: The power of colour

By Alix Lawson
Managing Director, **Lawson Robb**

Alix Lawson and Charlotte Robb formed Lawson Robb in 2003 to raise the bar in communicative design and delivery to an exceptional standard. Rather than enforcing a typical 'practice style', LAWSON ROBB tailor to the specific brief, tastes and specific lifestyle requirements of each client or developer's target market. Alix studied Architectural interior Design at The Inchbald School of Design, London in 2000. Alongside Charlotte Robb. Alix has over 10 years experience in the high-end residential market, as well as experience in Hotel Design. Alix's expertise within the company is her in depth knowledge of FF and e suppliers, products and her design direction of the company and projects undertaken. Here, Alix explores the development and application of colour and texture in textiles and fabrics.

The development and advancement of unusual finishes and how they can be applied has definitely had an impact on design schemes. The use of metal and stone is especially prominent and consequently has had an effect on the choice of colour and fabric. As the statement pieces and focus of the room is increasingly moving towards intense metallic finishes over large areas, colours are staying muted but warm in order to create equilibrium with the colder, powerful finishes.

Neutrals are still predominant and make a great backdrop for adding colour or artwork and strong interesting finishes, and can be updated and changed easily. But neutrals are also evolving into much stronger

Above: Lawson Robb have created an atmospheric interior for The Lancasters project

Above: The Canary Wharf project completed by Lawson Robb depicts a sumptuous use of colour and texture

versions - rich browns, ochre, deeper colours, all creating more of a statement. Warm tones such as mocha, bronze, cinnamon and cream will feature prominently. Native patterns marry well with shadow tones and pearlescent accents.

Chocolates and bronzes seem to be the colours du jour and people are experimenting with new hard finishes. A recent

example is an acid treated stone tabletop where they have used acid to melt the soft part of the stone in order to create textures for the stone, producing a leather look with a matt finish on a stone. Lacquers, bronzes and metals with depth and texture as opposed to flat wood are consistently asked for. Use of hard finishes has really evolved the last few years and we are constantly

developing new finishes.

At Lawson Robb we have found that the fundamental principle for successfully creating an atmospheric interior for a room that has a dark colour scheme is to incorporate texture and pattern, which brings depth, flavour and character to your overall scheme. Combining and layering contrasting textures is integral to designing an interior

Wendy Cushing Passementerie

Glass Tieback   **Avante Garde collection**   **Murano collection**

Above: Using darker accents with shiny finishes and contrasting textures, the room still looks open and inviting

that will not appear flat and void of visual interest. A lack of layers can lead to an impersonal, unwelcoming space.

Pattern and texture are so closely related that they can often project the illusion that one is doing the duty of the other. Contrast within textural differences ensures a powerful impact. By using a combination of different textures on walls and in fabrics you can make an interior with one dark palette interesting and dynamic rather than employing flat colour. Layering similar tones across different mediums makes a space feel bigger. Layering textures within the same colour palette gives energy to the room. You can layer the same tone but with varied textures and textiles.

We often use specialist wall finishes and hand crafted wallpaper to inject vibrancy within a dark room. We use a company that specialises in architectural metal finishes and metal coatings using cold-sprayed metal.

Pairing metallic elements within a dark scheme adds a sophisticated depth – hammered bronze metal cladding for doors and mirror frames, polished plaster and metallic particles in paint finishes are frequent features within our schemes. Lacquer finishes and unusual textures, such as, shagreen wallpaper, hand trawled wall finishes, grass wallpaper and snakeskin are perfect to add vibrant intense touches of interest.

We have used relief stone, hand trawled wall finishes or back lit onyx in bathrooms and hand chiselled stone in spas to introduce a tactile element. Often bathrooms are fit out in marble which can lead to a shallow, one – dimensional space.

Lighting is extremely important – with our darker schemes, we have installed mirror in key positions to reflect and refract light. Large mirrors and metallic elements bounce light around a space, which adds heavily to the atmospheric feel. Antiqued mirror is a stunning way to reflect light in a more diffused and subtle way. The varying intensities of both different strengths of light and metallic elements lead to an evolved, effortless look.

www.lawsonrobb.com

"Hammered bronze metal cladding for doors and mirror frames, polished plaster and metallic particles in paint finishes are frequent features within our schemes."

Tissus d' Hélène Ltd

Trend: Aspirational home design

By Inge Moore
Principal, **HBA London**

Inge began her career in South Africa working in museum design where she collaborated with Museum Africa to build the country's first post-apartheid museum before going on to lead the interior design department of an architectural practice in the creation of six prestigious super-casinos over six years. Since joining HBA London in 2001, Inge has been key in establishing the studio as one of the hospitality industry's most innovative and trendsetting interior design practices. Following her promotion to Managing Associate in 2006, and then to Principal in 2008, she moved the team's offices into an historic former theatre, a design environment that reflects and nurtures her team's creative inspiration. Inge believes that hotel interiors should have a narrative – a framework for the concept and a source for the design details, which together excite an emotional reaction that makes guests feel cared for while inviting a journey of discovery, which is engaging and fun. Here, Inge lends her expertise of hotel design to the subject of creating a home away from home. How can we transform spaces through examples of commercial and residential projects?

The philosophies behind the design of hospitality and residential spaces are increasingly converging. The aspirational qualities of high-style hotels have the ability to transport us to a "dream world" that might be quite different from our day-to-day experiences. Yet they also inspire the style of our homes, and conversely, our homes influence how we design hotels. The exchange of ideas between the two is much freer, with less "rules" than were in place in the past. Regardless, comfort reigns supreme. A hotel might have an avant-garde décor, use rare materials or be kitted-out with the latest technology, but no matter what the surroundings, the ability to simply relax and feel cared for is the most important

Above: The Sea Hotel Bat Yam atrium is spectacular but with comfortable, home style seating at the same time.

Above: St Regis Rome has a bespoke environment similar to those created at home

attribute of a luxury destination.

This blurring between residential and hospitality atmospheres means that the ideas used to create vast hotel spaces now translate more easily into a home setting. For example, the idea of zoning a hotel lobby into spaces with intimate seating groups is something that can be done in one's own living room so that when entertaining, there are options for having both private chats as well as larger group conversations. In hotels, we also love to play with proportion – using an oversized piece of art or a grand mirror creates a greater sense of drama and surprise than using smaller scale items.

Adopting this idea into one's home introduces an instant "wow" factor. One large fabulous painting or sculpture can potentially make a stronger impact than 10 assorted pieces. This is what we are doing for the lobby atrium of the Sea Hotel in Bat Yam, Israel. In partnership with a local artist, we are designing a soaring metal screen with abstract fretwork inspired by the biblical narrative of the crossing of the Red Sea.

Attention-to-detail is everything when designing a luxury hotel. Every facet is important and we spend lots of time making sure each one is exactly right - it's all these perfect

elements that add-up to a gorgeous design. It comes down to the finest of points – how tightly the carpet is tufted and the backing that is used, where the stone is sourced from and how it is honed, the thread count in a fabric and the types of dyes used, the dovetail joints in the timber tables and the kind of glue that holds them together, how the frame of the sofa is constructed and the way the tufts are sewn, etc...by being meticulous and thorough in our planning and having the highest quality standards for the materials and furnishings we specify, we can be confident that our end result will be exquisite and will endure in the years to come. Homeowners can do this as well. By researching how items are made, they will know they are getting the best quality for their money.

Many of the detailed touches, which give hotels their "polished" feel would also work well in a residence. For instance, our design of the Couture Suite in the St. Regis Rome has been inspired by Valentino, whose fashion house was founded in the "Eternal City" in 1965 and who used to unveil his celebrated collections in the hotel's ballroom. Our vision was to weave Valentino's hallmark flowing shapes with the meticulous details found in his dressmaking into the interior décor. One of the ways in which we achieved this was to add nailhead trim to the timber panelling and millwork. Reminiscent of the detailed embellishment one might find on a hand-tailored garment, this effect adds to sense of "couture" and is something that could easily be done in a home to add a high-style touch.

We also like to borrow ideas from residential bathrooms to create calming, comfortable experiences in hotels. A good example of this can be seen with the bathroom we designed for the Hotel Maria Cristina, a Luxury Collection property in San Sebastian, Spain. Here, we have plenty of freestanding shelves so that lotions and potions don't have to clutter the vanity counter. The tub is enveloped by a black and white striped shower curtain and next to it is a stack of nesting tables that can be rearranged to hold toiletries, candles, or even a bucket of Champagne. A pendant light forged from black iron feels more decorative than the typical functional lighting so often found in hotels. Adding

imaginative illumination to one's bathroom at home definitely boosts the luxury-factor - a sparkling chandelier really casts an aura of glamour.

The addition of unexpected and eclectic touches within the décor is another secret for making a hotel feel like a home-away-from-home. A scattering of small framed photos, a mixture of furniture styles and unmatched nightstands, and handmade objects from local artists are all ways to make a hotel room feel personal to the people using it. Sometimes, in an effort to make their home feel "high-style", people mistakenly believe they shouldn't display their family heirlooms and portraits. Although they don't

need to be used all at once, these keepsakes can be very powerful in creating the restorative hearth of a home. By bringing some of these symbols into the luxury hotel setting, we can help give guests the sense they are being cared for and pampered.

www.hbadesign.com

"Keepsakes can be very powerful in creating the restorative hearth of a home."

Above: Hotel Maria Cristina is a good example of the blurring of residential and commercial design lines

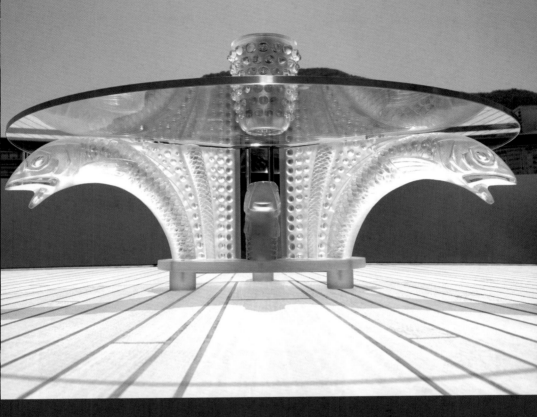

Trend: Personalising your home

By Rebecca Tucker and Helen Fewster

Directors, **Suna Interior Design**

Suna Interior Design is a boutique interior design consultancy in South London. Personable and highly committed to every detail of the design process, they have a vast knowledge of creating polished penthouses, bespoke apartments, attractive public spaces, stunning show homes, and impressive marketing suites in central London and across the South. Driven by their urban target markets, they are sensitive to creating design and style to fit modern needs and desires, putting great importance on researching each new locality. They work closely and collaboratively with their clients on their design ideas, providing innovative solutions, constantly pushing the boundaries of functional design. They create contemporary and lifestyle affirming spaces and pride themselves on high quality finishes and their cultivation of long term client relationships. Here Rebecca and Helen talk about the importance of personalising spaces though bespoke and innovative concepts.

I n recent years interest in interior design has expanded to touch all areas of home and work life, and the result of this has been a move away from generic modern design and sparse minimalism. There is a surge towards more personalised, unique and bespoke products, from smaller suppliers who can afford the time to promote luxury, cultural connectivity and innovation in design and services.

At Suna Interior Design we believe that there is a power in the personal touches that you can apply to all design. Commissioning bespoke items has become a key priority, not just with designers where consideration of this has always been at the forefront, but also with clients and individuals, who

Above: Colour is a bold statement and really says something about the personality of a home

Above: This bedroom space in Arlington house is minimal yet comfortable with soft and textured fabrics

are realising and appreciating the benefit of bespoke.

When you want to achieve the maximum effect in a design, to make it stand out and to stamp a mark of ownership on it, consider bespoke items. Across all interiors, whether it be in a hotel, a restaurant or concierge area, a one-off item will radiate qualities that are resonant with quality, attention to detail and luxury. In the same vein, similar effects can be achieved in your own home, adding quirkiness and individuality that radiates warmth and personality.

There is an increased interest in sourcing from smaller more unique outlets, rather than purchasing items from big chain stores, as people seek out individual one-off pieces to decorate their homes. Bespoke designed items will denote the character of the individual or business as well as symbolising their distinctive personality. Added to this, the accessibility of

interesting unique products from smaller companies makes for a much easier sourcing process thanks to the internet and the rise of social media, which has revolutionised the way that interior designers and individuals can find products for their designs. Viral word of mouth through Twitter, Facebook, Pinterest and the like has become a key route to promote and source products, never has good customer service been more vital, positive and negative feedback will promptly and swiftly be dispensed and made very public!

Inspired individuality, personal touches and craftsmanship are being embraced, with ideals of strong design and unique results. This is greatly influenced by increased media coverage, through TV, media and the internet, which endorses the importance of interior design in the home. People are becoming more informed and imaginative about

what types of design would suit or even improve their lifestyle. Money is being spent more wisely on big and small ticket items. Longevity, craftsmanship and love of an item are becoming key purchasing decisions.

There is a lot of consideration and care that goes into sourcing and creating bespoke items, originality can create an identity that is unique to an individual or your business environment. For instance, in a boutique hotel a successful design is one that is full of eye-catching innovation that is welcoming, comfortable, and memorable to visiting customers, impacting on their experience and ultimately forming their perception that the hotel they chose was worthy of their custom, and lived up to their expectations.

A lot of design can be transient in nature. With changing trends, colours and materials need to be updated and refreshed regularly, but a unique bespoke item can stand the test of time. Its very originality puts it outside the confines of 'trends', which ultimately are born of innovation but tire quickly once a product is over used and commonly seen.

Over the past 10 years we have prided ourselves at Suna Interior Design on our ability to access products from a wide range of sources, always looking for new suppliers and never getting stuck in a 'house style' that defines and confines us. In all projects, from show homes and interior specification, to public spaces and hospitality and hotel interiors we look to the client, their brief, their market and the style that best represents all these elements. Each design is a result of a process of working and reworking, of opening the net and then closing it on the right product, the right wallpaper or paint colour, the best fabric or curtain treatment and then bringing it all together in a

cohesive design. We have commissioned bespoke artwork, designed individual items of furniture, worked on one-off wallpaper designs, up-cycled vintage furniture, produced personalised items that are unique to our clients and generally ensured that we are always moving forward and maintaining an awareness of new and inspired design, supporting small and large companies who have fabulous ideas, and encouraging innovation and imagination in our own team.

Interior Design is much more than just space design or product selection, it is the creation of a visual and physical experience, and how you harness that experience is directly influenced by the products that you combine together, by the items that you deem beautiful, functional, meaningful or representative of the client, and, of course, their client. This in turn will provoke a subliminal perception, in the end

user, of the business in whose premises they stand. The nature of that perception, whether it be positive or negative, is all down to the detail. The personal touches will separate your design from the rest, turning mediocre into magnificent.

www.sunainteriordesign.com

> **"There is an increased interest in sourcing from smaller more unique outlets, rather than purchasing items from big chain stores."**

Above: In this Loxford Showflat the headboard is bespoke

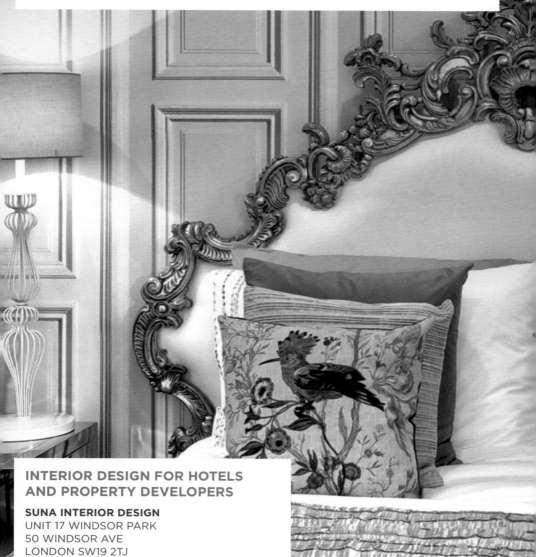

SU
—
NA

**INTERIOR DESIGN FOR HOTELS
AND PROPERTY DEVELOPERS**

SUNA INTERIOR DESIGN
UNIT 17 WINDSOR PARK
50 WINDSOR AVE
LONDON SW19 2TJ

020 8544 9350
INFO@SUNAINTERIORDESIGN.COM
SUNAINTERIORDESIGN.COM

image: Andrew Montgomery

Trend: Garden Design

By Charlotte Rowe
Founder, **Charlotte Rowe**

Charlotte originally trained as an Art Historian, working in the creative and media industries in London and Sydney before gaining a post-graduate diploma in Residential Landscape and Garden Architecture at the Oxford College of Garden Design (Oxford Brookes University). Charlotte has full accreditation and is a registered member of the Society of Garden Designers. With a background in professional consultancy and client service, Charlotte has a wealth of knowledge when it comes to working closely with clients on the development of the design brief. Here, Charlotte takes a look outside at the exciting world of garden design and lends her expertise to the subject of working with clients for a well-designed garden space.

Possibly because we have just lived through the wettest British Summer on record, one of the noticeable trends for 2012 was an increased interest in how to keep dry in the garden. Reflecting this, we have been providing overhead structures and shelter for gardens, though this also possibly part of a continuing desire to create outdoor rooms in cities. Outdoor kitchens have been really popular for the past three years and now everyone is asking for outdoor fireplaces and fire pits. We designed our first fireplace four years ago and during 2012 alone we were commissioned to design five gardens with fireplaces in London, the West Country and in Yorkshire. Fuelled by logs, gas or even bio ethanol they are a

Above: Charlotte Rowe, photographer - Andrew Montgomery

SureSet
Permeable Paving

The **Internal flooring** range from the resin bound paving specialists

Use the InBound range for a completely contemporary and modern alternative to traditional internal flooring. Virtually maintenance free and highly durable, the InBound range comes in a permeable or waterproof solution making it ideal for bathrooms, wet rooms, kitchens, playrooms and living areas throughout the home or office. **Available in a range of aggregates and over 30 colours all supplied and laid for you by our expert team.**

Now available in DIY Kits!
For more information or a free sample and quote, visit:
www.sureset.co.uk

Above: *Making use of rooftop spaces. Copyright Clive Nichols.*

wonderful way of creating a focal point in the garden and an all-year round entertainment area.

In terms of plants, the move is towards a looser, more relaxed planting style which we find works really well alongside the clean lines of the hard landscaping in our quite precise, carefully designed gardens. People want gardens, which are contemporary but they also want plants and 'green'. One of the best groups of plants to work in this style of garden are grasses which, combined with perennials, help soften the edges through the year.

How we work with clients

We have remained busy throughout the last three years but we find that people are increasingly seeking 'best value'

and a strong return on any investment in their garden. However, as in many walks of life, there is always a flight to quality in difficult times. It is important to remember that, while keeping things cost sensitive, beautiful, well-designed gardens add value to property.

We based our client relationships on a mutual understanding that expectations on both sides must be managed. We try to be as up-front as possible about likely costs and budget even from the first telephone conversation with a potential client. We like clients to be fully aware of the budgetary parameters of their particular project and we can design for them knowing that we are working within the designated budget.

In terms of the design brief, we try and tease as much out as possible but clearly it is always a relationship, which develops organically throughout the project. Each garden needs to complement and reflect the rest of the property, inside and out. So we try to mirror some or all of the elements of the interior design and exterior architecture in our designs. This will include materials such as stone paving, render and plastering styles and even lighting. We also strive to reflect the colour palette of the interiors in furnishings or planting in the garden.

British clients have normally grown up with a garden or have already had a garden of their own so they are much more plant-aware than our overseas clients who may never have had a garden before, have little or no knowledge or understanding and are somewhat overawed by the number and range of plants available in the UK (upwards of 10,000 different plants can be sourced and used in this country). So we make a point of preparing full planting plans and schedules with mood boards showing all plants, through the seasons. To a large extent, their decisions have to be based on trust in us and our ability to choose the right plants for the right locations.

Town versus Country

For town gardens, we always design 'off' the house and the resulting designs are quite architectural in feel, balanced by lush planting. We always light our town gardens and roof terraces, either working on our own lighting plans or with lighting design specialists. Subtly lit gardens extend the use and life of a garden massively, creating an additional outdoor space to be looked at and enjoyed all year, day or night, doubling the value, which can be gained from having a garden.

In country gardens, we are working with a much larger canvas and palette and we also need to take account of the surrounding countryside - the borrowed landscape, which becomes the back drop for the garden design. So our design style tends to change to reflect this, becoming less structured and more plant-oriented.

Genius loci

Discovering the genius of the place is a principle at the heart of all decent landscape design but it is never more true than for projects overseas where weather patterns, soil profiles, horticultural heritages and light levels are totally different from

here in the UK. This is a unique challenge for garden designers, which differentiates us from interior designers and means that we do not take on projects overseas without extensive site visits.

We have worked in California, Northern Italy, Southern France and Saudi Arabia and work with local horticultural experts to ensure that the specialised planting palette required for that particular climate zone is used for each project. One of our biggest challenges was a project in Manhattan where we designed three roof terraces for a client with a converted dairy in Tribeca. All roof terraces are challenging for a number of reasons, not least the weather conditions, which prevail at a high level. However, roof

terraces in New York experience enormous fluctuations in temperature from boiling hot in the summer to snow and ice in the winter, which means that plants have to be really carefully chosen to withstand this.

The future

We will continue to design the urban gardens and roof terraces for which we are known but we are now being asked to work on increasing numbers of large scale landscape projects. One of the key challenges for larger gardens is to deal with the ever more random weather patterns hitting the UK. After a few years of dry summers and winters forcing us to look increasingly at drought tolerant plants, we have just had the wettest summer in memory.

Above: Charlotte commented, "we always design 'off' the house and the resulting designs are quite architectural in feel, balanced by lush planting." Copyright Charlotte Rowe Garden Design Light IQ

THE HEVENINGHAM COLLECTION

CALL +44 (0) 1489 893481 OR VISIT HEVENINGHAM.CO.UK
EMAIL: SALES@HEVENINGHAM.CO.UK

image: Alex Lake

Trend: Translating hotel design

By Tara Bernerd
Partner, **Tara Bernerd & Partners**

British Designer, Tara Bernerd is founder of the established interior architectural practice, Tara Bernerd & Partners. Working with an executive team of highly experienced architects and designers based out of the London Headquarters in Belgravia, the focus for Tara is on the relevance of creative direction and interior design. Tara's business interests continue to grow, working increasingly on a global platform with projects in New York, Chicago, London, Hong Kong and Switzerland. Key clients include Berkeley Homes, St George, the LeFraks, Thompson Group, MARC Restaurants, Blackstone, Center Parcs, Heron, Grosvenor Asia, amongst a select few and private clients who as always remain anonymous. Tara Bernerd & Partners' designs reflect intelligent space planning and layouts, with a strong use of texture and colour, which typify their projects. With a more edgy approach Tara's work is renowned for creating warmth and atmosphere. Increasingly focusing on the Hotel and Restaurant industries the practice is committed to making a difference through design. Here, Tara talks us through her experience of hotel design and how these concepts can be translated into the home.

Luxury, a word used increasingly that in many ways has been stretched beyond its origin, is a topic that I am drawn to. The essence of what is luxury and indeed looking into what luxury today is all about.

With creative direction as a distinctive part of our business, invariably our clients are not sure at all of the end look and feel - this includes restaurateurs, hoteliers and private clients - we are always required to be one step ahead in regard to an understanding of setting a brief, which often entails luxury today and how this translates into interiors.

Therefore we have to be on the pulse, plus have a strong instinct for what is current and

Above: Belgraves demonstrates Rough Luxury', opulent, yet relaxed and laid back in its appearance

Above: Marble, especially in this vein-ridden form is perfect for that opulent feel

what will stand the test of time. For although like fashion our industry is linked to style, taste and indeed shape it must wear well; and like the ultimate Chanel suit, we must defy the decades.

So what is luxury and more relevant what is luxury today? It's tempting to also become fairly philosophical too about the question of luxury, i.e. is it health, space, freedom? Of course it is!

So I intend to stick to my boundaries and as I am designer to ensure I keep to topic, focusing on the aesthetics not the philosophical.

However before we dive in let's consider, what is luxury literally? My immediate thoughts, instant reactions include: "ultimate comfort", "expensive", "impressive". The Cambridge Dictionaries on-line definition: great comfort, especially as provided by expensive and beautiful things.

However, recently whilst dining at Little House, a seductive restaurant in the heart of Mayfair, it occurred to me that it is an example of how I would describe "rough luxury" and that is where I intend to lead you. A

phrase often attributed to our own work at Belgraves.

For in my opinion there will always be a more traditional "grand luxury", however society has evolved and thus I would challenge so has luxury evolved and today is also about the emergence of rough luxury, or perhaps more palatable: informal luxury.

Informal luxury is certainly more current, thus arguably more appropriate to our times, and certainly less ostentatious. When pulled off successfully it is far more cool, seductive and in many ways more interesting. It's about making a hit, with punch and attitude, yet still with a strong regard to finishes and materials. Perhaps it's the mix of raw materials i.e. brick or reclaimed wood, mixed with plush velvets that combine a loft or industrial feel with traditional luxury. The outcome an informal evolution of luxury.

To be clear, there is no wrong or right way and there are countless examples of projects within our own portfolio where a more traditional look on occasion can be more appropriate.

Belgraves, set in the heart of Belgravia in London, is all about informal luxury; it is also a great example of how hotel design is an area that can be increasingly applied to our homes. Working in both worlds of hotels and residences the edges are blurred, from bedrooms to lounge seating there are certainly crossovers.

The entrance is a double-height space set to feel like a home-from-home, using marvellous grey wood floors, stones and a fireplace to greet you. The entrance is the first impression of any home or hotel.

The concierge area sees the continuation of wood floors and the leather wrapping around the columns, bespoke furniture and rugs. A glimpse into the many seating areas, this time a modern L-shaped sofa, a Linley club chair, with a beaded screen, to separate the lobby from the restaurant.

The staircase that leads up to the library, shows a departure from grand banisters, yet through glass, leather and bronze a sweeping staircase is created. From there, the library bar starts to embrace different materials

Above: One of the Belgraves bedrooms with a beautiful view and a homely feel to the interior

and a warmer palette, with a bespoke bookcase. The bar sees the use of mixed metals with the paler polished plaster walls providing a contrast.

The grey-decked terrace is small and understated. The restaurant – definitely here the use of ceramic tiled floors, wood and brickwork combines to bring a more New York feel. Upstairs the corridors are fairly simple, with the introduction of a bespoke carpet. Bedrooms –

Although there is use of colour and texture, the departure from chintz allows for a more monotone feel, yet fabrics, contemporary furniture and the layering of rugs still bring warmth in a more modern approach. Bathrooms – where the use of traditional stone in a modern manner is merged with the addition of the grey woods and smoked glass creating the vanity units.

The materials used

throughout all these interiors are all carefully considered to bring an understated sense of luxury.

Ironically, or perhaps accurately, this evolution is witnessed across numerous creative industries from film, to fashion, to furniture and antiques and like any true evolution it is not unique to the world of interiors alone; the luxury revolution continues.

www.tarabernerd.com

Above: Mixing sofa fabrics with contrasting rugs and cluttering a room up can still be luxurious

Design Spotlight

The design spotlight is designed to cast a light on some of the trends and concepts that have been taking the design world by storm. Great British design has been a much talked about subject in the year of 2012 and this pattern of emerging British talent is set to continue for some time. Our designers talk about what design means to them as well as touching on the subject of International design and sourcing great products for the home.

putting the designers under the spotlight...

Asifa Tirmizi

Galina Ginzburg-Maly

Lindsey Rendall

Nathan Hutchins

Ros Wilson

Scot R. Campbell

Susan Knof

Victoria Stainow

Vincent Kirk

Above: Injecting patriotic colours into the home for that truly British feel. Roselind Wilson Design.

Design Spotlight: Best of British

What epitomises great British design?

Vincent Kirk: British design walks the tightrope of tradition and innovation so well because we love the look and feel of old houses, yet we insist on comfort – and we love gadgets! The best modern houses use natural materials in new ways and incorporate super-smart technologies. Seth Stein Architects' Pencalenick House in Cornwall is a great example of this and uses materials, which could have come from the site itself, in strict geometries, filled with natural light. Heaven!

Victoria Stainow: To me, the Best of British design is still its great country houses, ideally with a garden designed by Capability Brown.

Susan Knof: For me, great British design is best epitomised by a mix of design, craftsmanship, and considerate production. Post-war British products evolved from new materials and processes that were often developed in the war. Great designers, like Robin and Lucienne Day introduced furniture and textiles which were instrumental in the transformation of British design after World War II. It was only in the 1950s that design began to be identified as a profession. However, the post-war reorganisation of the Royal College of Art allowed for students to be trained specifically to design the products needed by British industry.

Asifa Tirmizi: British Design for me epitomises a perfect balance between tradition and contemporary design. When visiting friends and family in the UK, I am always impressed by the mix of old eclectic pieces with some sleek modern ones.

Lindsey Rendall: Great Britain may be a small nation but in the design world we are giants. A nation with such a rich and exciting history as ours could be nothing but powerful leaders in style and design. As a nation we travelled the globe bringing back textiles, spices, furniture, art, food and other exotic treasures to stimulate our senses. Due to our tolerant society we also became a safe destination for many cultures

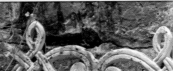

Above: The Intercontinental Park Lane Hotel in London, designed by HBA shows how London has embraced British designs.

amazing textile technology design ensured all kits were tailored to support the athletes in their individual discipline. Danny Boyle's opening ceremony was full of imagination, humour, music, and craftsmanship. Our Olympians displayed skill, talent and most of all sheer determination, all qualities I'd expect to find in great design.

There is today and always has been an exciting edgy buzz surrounding British design, an energy source which ebbs and flows but never seems to falter. With designers working across the UK in small garden craft studios to large city based firms it is this diverse, energetic and continually creative scene, which still makes Britain a destination of choice for artisans and designers alike. Our rich historic past and ever evolving surroundings ensure we'll never run out of inspiration or craftsman to create really great British Designs.

Ros Wilson: Britain is rich in culture and heritage, which is reflected in the many eras of beautiful architecture. The cultural diversity of the country has allowed a constant flow of talent and ideas over time resulting in highly creative design solutions that juxtapose classic features with contemporary finishes to showcase design that is truly British. A good example of this would be the recently completed refurbishment works to the St Pancras Grand. Here, superior skill and craftsmanship has allowed for the restoration of every detail of a truly spectacular building which is exquisitely offset by the best in materials and finishes so that this building can now stand as a beacon of pride for British Design. Ironically this landmark stands at the gateway to Europe.

and as a result, like the English language which has the richest vocabulary of any language, we have developed over hundreds of years, a design style which encompasses all these influences, embroiders them together like a rich tapestry and somehow produces something which can only be described as very British.

It's not only our eclectic style, which makes British design great, it is our wonderful skill, ingenuity and craftsmanship. Irrespective of the subject, Furniture, Textiles, Art, Fashion, Design, Film, Industry, Technology, Music or Architecture, we produce things thoughtfully, skillfully, sympathetically and imaginatively whether it is a length of woven silk, a film, a building or a piece of industrial machinery.

Our British design power was fantastically illustrated this year at the 2012 Olympics. The Velodrome, designed by Hopkins Architects and engineered by Expedition along with the Aquatic centre, designed by Architects Zaha Hadid both made a strong, powerful impression within the Olympic park complex; the fluidity of movement suggested by the elegant flowing lines of the buildings captured their interior purpose perfectly. Stella McCartney's Olympic kit designs were symbolic, strong and empowering whilst remaining understated and demure. The

Above: Villa Rosinka Lounge, Moscow by SHH shows bold design concepts

Design Spotlight: International design

What influences are we set to see coming over from International seas and how can we embrace these trends?

Vincent Kirk: One area where Europe is still way ahead of the UK is in low and zero-carbon design, presenting British designers with countless examples of cool, environmentally-friendly living. We believe the British soul, however, is a more complex thing and that we need to provide style and comfort along with cool minimalism. What we are working on now is how to take the principles of Passivhaus, which allow us to design houses which need little or no artificial heating, but to adapt them to suit the particular look that our

British clientele wants. As Passivhaus develops in this country, it is being adapted to a wider range of applications than just the conventional new-build box, which does not suit everybody or every location. It can even be adopted in part via extensions and annexes, bringing it to a wider audience, appreciative of the massive reduction in energy bills!

Susan Knof: The international influences I think we are set to see are more use of colour, pattern, texture - all with an emphasis on handicraft. Ideas and fashions have constantly flowed from country to country and from East to West. Nowadays, not only is international travel more accessible to the masses, but one

can also travel 'virtually' with the aide of the internet. Global ideas, techniques, and inspiration are ever flowing. The explorer Marco Polo introduced the West to the exotic styles of the Far East with his descriptive accounts of foreign travels and triggered an explosion of Chinese influence on Western ideas and design, including the use of lacquer, fretting, oriental motifs and pagodas. He was one explorer whose travels inspired many. Now the cross-pollination of ideas, styles, and techniques is large scale and instantaneous. This makes the future of design exciting and limitless.

Asifa Tirmizi and Scot R.Campbell: We will continue to see more of a natural, "handmade" look influence for all types of interior design products from furniture to flooring to fabrics. We will also continue to see an influence of fresh ideas for sustainable products.

Lindsey Rendall: Over the past few of years we have broadened our horizons in search of crafted pieces and as a result have seen an eclectic trend developing and an increase of international influence particularly in the textiles industry. At Decorex 2012 many of the fabric houses had launched a creative mix of multi-cultural textures and patterns. The style I'm most drawn to are the beautiful, exotic Ikat designs. Ikat is a dying technique used to pattern textiles dating back to the 10th century and widely used across the Middle East, South East Asia, Japan and central America. Although an ancient technique the fabrics are kept current and relevant, woven in wonderful colours such as vibrant pinks and acid yellows through to muted greys and natural hues. One of my personal favourites is Simla by Zoffany, a subtle design, which could be worked into traditional or contemporary interior schemes alike. Ikat designs are just one example of fabrics with international influence. These exciting, heavily patterned and adorned textiles are enriching our fashion style, injecting some life and soul into our interior schemes.

Introducing this trend into an existing interior is simple to do; the wide variety and scales of pattern on offer will ensure you can use a design, which will sit comfortably within your existing scheme. The huge colour spectrum of designs available enables you to pick subtle tones to effortlessly blend, or vivid bright designs, which pack a

Above: Hotel Maria Cristina by HBA London

punch in an otherwise subtle scheme. You can gently bring in small pieces of ethnic or tribal crafted pieces. Persian rugs will add instant ethnic flair to any interior and can be sourced in a wide range of colours and patterns. Create a statement piece by re-upholstering a key item of furniture in a large scale design or by adding a leading edge or contrast section to an existing pair of plain curtains.

To prevent the scheme from taking on a hippy, student edge, combine age old traditional designs with sleek, contemporary lines. Mix them with simple, modern shaped pieces of furniture and neutral soft wall colours to create an eclectic, inspiring interior with longevity.

Ros Wilson: Design derives influences from a multitude of sources but notably there are many beautiful ideas, products and finishes integrating themselves into the local palette and mood boards of designers. Intricate patterns of typically Moroccan ceramics can add warmth and personality to modern bathrooms. Equally there continues to be trend in the use of patterned rugs to add character to an interior. These patterns take inspiration from the East and are large and oversized, not too small and fussy. Staying with the influences from the East, the battered metal and earthenware from countries like Thailand add a sense of warmth and ground an interior. When reviewing the design of an interior, don't be afraid to experiment with these exciting finishes. Simply complement your existing look by changing the rug, painting the walls or adding a selection of earthenware to the coffee table, to give the room a new look and feel.

"Now the cross-pollination of ideas, styles, and techniques is large scale and instantaneous. This makes the future of design exciting and limitless." Susan Knof

Above: *Pod House - a curved timber 'pod' was bespoke-designed and then pre-fabricated and craned onto site, providing additional living space. Image by KKE Architects*

Design Spotlight: Individuality

What would you say is the key to creating a personal touch in the home? What would be your one tip for getting it right?

Vincent Kirk: I'd love to say there is a single tip that's good for all, but the true embodiment of a person's individual vision is usually the result of a long, on-going dialogue between the client and the designer. We regard the taking of the brief - and its development throughout the project – as being of the greatest importance. Only when we really know how our client thinks, can we be sure we will make the right decisions and offer solutions, which fit perfectly. On a more superficial styling level, collected items from people's travels or beautiful organic items from nature always personalise an interior really well.

Victoria Stainow: The key is not to try to do everything at once. Take time to build the room, finding the right pieces over time. Special pieces of furniture, art and lighting make such a difference. Mix periods and styles, fabric motifs, and make sure not all the colours go together perfectly, don't try to reproduce a hotel room! The interior should look as if it has evolved over time, rather than put together in a week.

Nathan Hutchins: I think we need to change our perception of design and understand that it is not defined by objects, but rather by our experiences around these objects. The spaces where we spend time help shape our memories – it's an intuitive response of human nature. Our environment is created by the way these individual objects come together to holistically evoke an emotional reaction – and in our homes, this should be the feeling of being special and cared for. My tip is that that it's important for these ingredients to be added to the mix over time so that our spaces feel "collected" and are a story of our life experiences. It's a mistake to go to the shop and buy everything all at once. Designing a space with furnishings, artwork, mementos etc, that spark fond memories is what transforms a house into a home.

Susan Knof: In order to create an interior with a personal touch, you have to be true to yourself. As a designer, I make a lot of design suggestions. I share inspirations, ideas, and thoughts. But what makes it personal is when the space starts to reflect the priorities of how the clients want to use the space, which starts to dictate the layout. Meanwhile, their hobbies, collections, colours, and existing furniture help to allow the tactile element of the property to evolve.

I recently did a property for a young international couple and suggested incorporating a bold black and white text feature wall in their cloakroom using hand-cut Nero Marquina marble with all text inset in natural-finish Cromatica Super Branco, hand-cut in Italy. Although I presented the initial concept, I requested that the clients provide the text as it was important that their home reflected their values and what is meaningful to them. They chose the words 'omne ignotum pro magnifico est' (all that is unknown seems beautiful).

In another recently completed property (for an English family with five daughters), I was asked to create a room for each child, which represented their distinct personalities. The end result was a series of youthful rooms for a princess and her twin sister (the tomboy), to a bohemian room in a series of aqua tones with her own carved out daybed. Lastly, there was a bedroom for the fashonista daughter with Marimekko curtains and Diane Von Furstenberg wall covering in the walk in wardrobe. The process was light-hearted and fun and the result very colourful.

Asifa Tirmizi and Scot R.Campbell: The key to 'successfully' creating a personal touch is to not overdue it, many

Above: Even the children's bedroom is a great opportunity to show some individuality

times a client loves a certain colour or print and would like to use it throughout the project and it's just gets to be overkill. With that said, a personal touch in a home is extremely important, some ways that we address it, is by picking an interest or feature that the client is passionate about and applying it to the project. This can be abstractly or even somewhat literally. We once had a client that had a wonderful collection of vintage music albums, so we used images of some of them to create custom wallpaper that we used on one wall in a media room. The one tip for getting it right - keep it simple!

Lindsey Rendall: We all have slightly different taste; even dedicated followers of fashion will put their own spin on a style thus making it work for them. When designing your own home the most important thing is that you'll love spending time within the completed environment you create. The key is to stay true and faithful to your own style likes and interests and weave these carefully into your scheme.

A good interior designer should be able to take any pieces which have a personal value to you whether it is a family heirloom, a piece of artwork that you love, a collection of crockery or something as simple as a colour and use this as a focal point within your design.

For an enthusiastic antiques collector who may move from a traditional period home into a contemporary apartment; use your wonderful collection of antique furniture, artwork and rugs; mix them with sleek contemporary sofas and soft furnishings and use a pale grey wall tone as a neutral background and suddenly your beloved pieces will take on a new life, their age old elegance standing proud against the new interior. The same principle would work for collectors of any objects whether they are collections of glass, mirrors, artwork, dolls or parts of machinery, design a simple backdrop for your treasured belongings, light them well and they will add character to any space.

For colour fanatics, use blocks of colour to create dramatic effect rather than overloading your scheme. You do not need a lot of colour if using a bright tone to achieve striking effects, be selective and restrained to gain maximum results. A row of vivid coloured china cups in a white kitchen will make a bigger statement than multi coloured walls. Draw colours from a piece of art or decorative rug and use this as an accent throughout your scheme.

Most importantly your design needs to reflect you and your taste; stay true to this as it is the personal details that allow an interior to evolve into a home.

Ros Wilson: When designing your space, never lose sight that you are designing it for yourself, it is an extension of your own personality and for you to truly love it, it must represent a space

that you feel happy, calm and at peace. To get it right, go with your gut on any decisions you make. You will be pleasantly surprised at how well you know yourself and the results it will render.

Above: Ros Wilson has displayed a bold stamp of individual creative thinking in this fabulous bathroom interior

CATTO GALLERY

Catto Gallery has been established since 1986 and has grown to become one of the most prestigious fine art galleries in London. We specialise in the best of contemporary art across all mediums. Using our unique combination of expertise and resources we work with architects and interior designers to deliver inspirational places to live and work in. We have a large art collection that is ideally suited to creating an immediate visual impact and the unique finishing touch to a home or office. Please contact Iain, Imogen or Kate for further details.

100 Heath Street • Hampstead • London NW3 1DP
Tel: +44 (0)20 7435 6660 • www.cattogallery.co.uk • art@cattogallery.co.uk

Opening times: 10am - 6pm Mon - Sat • 12.30pm - 6pm Sunday • and by appointment

Above: Here Lucia Caballero has presented figures from pop culture to elevate that 'cool' vibe

Design Spotlight: Popular culture

What influences can you see coming in from film and television when thinking about design? How can clients incorporate this into their own homes?

Vincent Kirk: Our clients have been known to cite particular movies when explaining their vision for a house, especially for interiors where their particular eclectic vision can be hard to articulate. A recent example was '...like the beach-house from 'Something's Gotta Give..." It is a really good shortcut in trying to understand where the client is coming from. We do not dismiss all TV makeover shows as some designers do; Kirsty Allsop is rarely wide of the mark and Kevin McCloud has single-

handedly opened up modernism to a wider audience.

Gale Ginzburg-Maly: Films inspire many trends in design. Often they are a whim, en vogue for only a season or that is already "out" after fashion week. Others spark a more permanent influence on our surroundings, and usually these styles come from films set in earlier times.

When a great period film is released, the worlds of fashion and interior design are often quick to follow. In this noisy, crowded and technology-filled age, the subconscious inclination of city dwellers is to create homes having a quiet, tidy and comfortable ambience. And that's what period films do so well – they evoke nostalgia for more formal and elegant times. This

influence, partnered with the desire for a sophisticated urban lifestyle, translates into a trend for residences with traditional, high-quality design and tasteful arrangements.

The relationship between Hollywood and fashion, whether it's couture or interior décor, was more literal in previous decades. Stores rushed to reproduce memorable costumes and designers based their entire collections on the silver screen. Nowadays the influence that film brings to design is more oblique, with subtle expressions conveyed, for example, through abstract impressions, colours or moods. Yet the motion picture industry remains a rich and constant reference point and source of inspiration for designers. Unknowingly or not, a film's colours and sensory imprints linger in our minds as part of a vast bank of images that may re-surface at any time to fuel our imagination.

When it comes to incorporating a style from a film into your own living room, it's better to capture the essence of its attractive qualities through a few simple gestures rather than recreate the movie set. Adopting a scene's predominant colour palette, integrating a handful of signature accessories, or focusing on key pieces of furniture will allow a home to be infused with the spirit of a film instead of feeling like a museum.

Susan Knof: I think we have already started to see an extraordinary amount of influence coming in from both film and television. 'Madmen' shows mid-century modern design in a glamorous, high profile setting with New York as the backdrop. Another example is the period drama, Downtown Abbey, which depicts the lives, inclusive of their interiors, of an aristocratic British family in the post-Edwardian era. The effect? Think rich velvets, patissimenterie, decadence, tassels, gold-leaf finishes, gilted mirrors and rich mahogany furniture creating what some call a "new traditionalism". A film that I think is set to make its mark on interiors is the latest Bond film, Skyfall. It depicts a collaboration of styles, which are actually already well under way. Clients can easily incorporate film, TV, and media in their own interiors by having a trusting relationship with their interior designer and by providing their source of inspiration. I would love a client to make this request! It isn't limited to film or television. How dynamic would it

be to create an interior inspired by the ballet, opera, or theatre?

Asifa Tirmizi and Scot R.Campbell: We occasionally get clients saying that they want their space to look similar to something they have seen on TV. Generally, it's certain colours or decorative elements, not so much spatial configurations, so it's easy for a client to incorporate with simple cosmetic changes.

Lindsey Rendall: As individuals we are constantly being molded by our surrounding environments and the situations we experience. The media of film and television has always made a strong impact in the design industry and been influential towards interior styling. The art of film making transports us into another world; it allows us to experience the past and the future, to experience glamour or poverty, romance or war and to feel in touch with other cultures and societies. When a connection is felt or we've been inspired by a film it is understandable to want to bring elements of this experience into our homes which then enable us to recreate and relive the emotions time and time again. An example of this was the trend towards Indian textiles and artwork following the release of 'Slumdog Millionaire' directed by Danny Boyle in 2008. It would be unlikely to create an entire Indian interior but the subtle introduction of textiles in the form of throws, cushions and rugs or Indian items of furniture would provide a flavour of the exotic experienced within the film.

The biggest influence from film during the past 100 years I believe comes from the glamorous Hollywood era of the 1920's through to the late 1950's.

The opulent style and sharp smart fashion tailoring; sophisticated feminine shapes and glamorous textures created a design style which epitomised elegance and class. Post war as a nation we aspired to be a part of something we were not accustomed to and therefore Britain was greatly seduced by America and the allure of Hollywood glamour as seen on the silver screen.

The buzz of chic elegance, excitement and luxury from this era is still very prevalent today. A touch of Hollywood charm can be injected into our interior designs by integrating marble and stone for kitchen worktops and within our bathrooms. Using opulent fabrics such as; velvets, silks and leathers in muted powder candy shades and metallic tones. The use of metal, mirror, glass and stone inlaid within our wooden furniture pieces. By hanging oversized mirrors and decorative glass chandeliers and finishing curvaceous upholstery pieces with beautiful deep buttoning detail.

Ros Wilson: Design can closely follow the latest trends in television and film. We live in a society where the element of belonging drives our behavioural patterns. If a particular TV series or film is widely accepted, it can influence current behavioural trends and so forth. An example would be the popularity of the TV Series Mad Men, which saw a return to modern retro fashion and interiors with the use of a palette of dusty blues, greys and greens offset by rich timbers with gentle curves and subtle detailing. Fabrics become simple with clean lines. The look becomes slick, confident and assertive with a dash of fun.

Above: *This luxury Townhouse in Hyde Park was designed by SHH*

Design Spotlight: Luxury

What in your opinion defines luxury design and how can clients achieve it?

Vincent Kirk: Luxury above all comes from a sense of space - and spaciousness - especially where it is unexpected - in entrance halls, connecting spaces, stairs and so on. Wonderful connections between inside space and outside create a sense of boundless luxury, which we believe has a more fundamental impact on the way we live than traditional luxurious effects dependant on the use of exotic materials.

Victoria Stainow: I think quality of craftsmanship is the ultimate luxury. Quality lasts and sometimes "luxury" doesn't.

Invest in one good piece rather than three mediocre. Less is more!

Susan Knof: To me luxury is about quality and good design, not necessarily expenditure. I work in the luxury market and I believe it's essential to create an interior that meets both functional and aesthetic requirements. This requires that the overall layout works with highly coordinated lighting (natural and artificial), integrated mechanical and electrical control systems and landscape design, to the finishing of the interior layout, design, decoration and the styling that epitomises luxury. Yes, luxury can come in the form of materiality. I have been told before that I have champagne taste. I do love rich marbles, gold

leafing, gilted finishes, eglomise mirrors, mohairs, high thread counts, mother of pearl finishes, fine cashmeres, wools, silks, textured metals and embossed leathers - which can all be rather costly. However, a good luxury interior design can work within the client's budget, allocating these decadent materials in small doses to offer a level of refined opulence.

The experience of an interior truly defines its luxury. A layout that doesn't work is going to provide constant frustration. An ill-proportioned chair is never going to feel luxurious, no matter whether it's gilted or upholstered in the finest cut-pile silk velvet.

Asifa Tirmizi and Scot R.Campbell: In our opinion, well made, well-constructed designed details equal luxury. It goes a long way to focus on some architectural details that often get overlooked. For example, in contemporary renovations baseboards, door frames and doors are often disregarded. If a client truly wants to achieve luxury design than the details that define a space must be designed well first.

Lindsey Rendall: The subject of luxury is a comparative one as for each of us the boundary between luxury and normality differs greatly. With our economy still precariously balanced, an increasing number of people are finding their everyday items and in some cases even jobs, becoming treasured luxuries rather than expected commodities.

Luxury design doesn't have to be an interior scheme filled with expensive objects, bespoke furniture, rich textiles, marble and original artwork; it can be a thoughtful and cleverly designed space which provides you with something you have little of. A simple example of this would be to compare first and standard class seating on an aeroplane, fundamentally your situation is equal, sitting on a plane heading to the same destination but the experience is worlds apart. The additional space and physical attention given in first class allows you feel indulged and therefore the journey is considered luxurious. Another example would be to give a child minder ten minutes of complete silence in the middle of a busy day or a night in a bed for a homeless person, both situations provide a sanctuary, a place of escape from daily life and therefore are luxurious.

For me the key to luxury design is to create an environment, which makes you feel indulged. This can be

Above: Ros Wilson brings drama and luxury to a cloakroom

achieved in many ways and through a variety of media without being financially crippling if executed using good quality materials and beautifully finished.

Invest in a piece of art, which gives you enjoyment day after day. Fit a deep piled carpet or invest in a beautiful rug, which feels decedent under foot. Purchase a wider bed so you can sleep in undisrupted comfort or have enough space to accommodate your family in the morning. Install under floor heating in your bathroom and a heated towel rail to prevent stepping out of a warm bath onto cold tiles or ever using a damp towel. Plan clever storage solutions in all rooms of your home, thus preventing clutter and the stresses associated with it. If you're a collector then design suitable ways to exhibit your treasured possessions. If you're a film fanatic create a home cinema experience. If you love being

outdoors blend your internal and external living spaces.

Having lived in London for many years and recently built a property in the Suffolk countryside my luxury is to open my bedroom curtains each morning to find not a building in sight!

Ros Wilson: Luxury design is defined by the synergy of perfect proportions, intricate detailing and tasteful finishes to create a sense of balance and harmony within a space. To achieve it start with one element that most inspires you or drives your desire for a space. Gain an understanding of what it is about that piece or element that you adore and start to build the scheme around this piece. Keep your palette refined and timeless and steer clear of trends of the moment as these will become outdated.

Above: Rendall and Wright 17th Century Surrey House project

Design Spotlight: Sourcing

Do you have any tips for sourcing furniture, fabrics, antiques and other items for the home?

Vincent Kirk: There is a growing selection of specialist reclamation and salvage companies sourcing and restoring items for clients directly, whilst Local Guilds of designer crafts-people are a rich seam for finding beautiful, unique and exciting work. You shouldn't be afraid either of talking directly to local artisan crafts-people to commission something really unique. Even if you only have a vague idea, it can be evolved together with them, which is a really exciting process, creating unique pieces of furniture, sculpture or fabric.

Victoria Stainow: For antiques, get to know a handful of dealers and develop a rapport; they are often a fountain of knowledge and one can really learn a lot. Buy only from people you trust.

Susan Knof: My tips for sourcing furniture, fabrics, antiques, and the odd curiosities is to always keep your eyes open. Curiosity may have killed the cat, so to speak, but curiosity makes the designer.

I love antique markets, furniture fairs, and stumbling upon an unusual shop when going off the beaten-path. I am always travelling and looking out for those one-of-a-kind pieces. I spend my time in both London and New York, where I heavily rely on the main design centres

such as Chelsea Harbour as well as the A&D and D&D buildings in New York. But it's when I find myself in far-flung destinations that my design senses are truly stimulated. This ranges from Parisian and Italian markets to Moroccan souks, Middle Eastern carpet suppliers, Indian and Thai fabric manufacturers and metal workers. I am anxious to make my way to Istanbul to let the Byzantine architecture lay the groundwork for some new inspiration!

Asifa Tirmizi and Scot R.Campbell: You can find almost anything on the internet these days…but it's hard for someone that is not in the design field to visualise what something will look like in person. Often what you see in a photo will look

Search over 100,000 antiques and works of art at the tip of your fingers

www.antiques.co.uk

BUY antiques ▪ SELL antiques ▪ LOVE antiques

different in person. My advice would be to get out a measuring tape and double check measurements of what you are planning to get versus the space where you will put it.

Lindsey Rendall: Sourcing products for interior design schemes is an exciting, addictive pastime and today we are spoilt for choice on places to look. There are of course high street retail stores selling mass produced furnishings. Beautiful boutiques selling bespoke interior products and many interiors outlets on a sliding scale in between. For hunting out something slightly quirky or unusual you may want to search off the beaten track.

Long gone are the days of creeping into garage sales or rubbish dumps to quickly purchase, and then secrete objects which would reappear, restored and looking glorious at a later date with the source of the purchase remaining a closely guarded secret. We have entered an era where environmental responsibility and cradle to grave philosophy is of huge importance in manufacturing and production and as a knock on effect re-cycling and up cycling; buying vintage and receiving second hand goods is considered cool and chic. Reinventing objects and breathing new life into them or picking up a bargain gives us a feeling of achievement along with a warm glow of thrifty satisfaction.

If you are lucky enough to live near a working fabric mill or furniture manufactures visit the factory outlet shop, which is usually on site. You can often find gorgeous textiles or hand crafted furniture at a reduced rate due to being slightly flawed, sample pieces or end of line designs. Craft fairs or student shows are brilliant

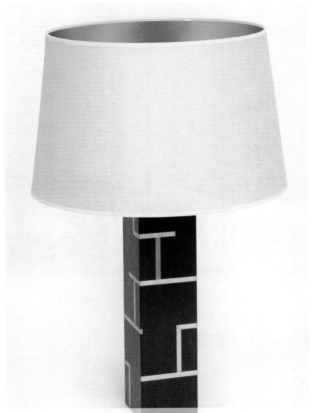

Above: Victoria Stainow demonstrates that in sourcing, sometimes you choose beauty over function

opportunities to pick up one off pieces, which may turn out to be wise investments in the future.

Many organisations such as Freecycle and Gumtree enable you to search and pick up items at little or no cost at all. Pop up shops, Antique fairs and car boot sales alike. If searching for items to up cycle look beyond the condition it may currently be in, look at the shape and form of the piece, imagine it restored and re-upholstered or utilised in a different way. Try not to make purchases purely based on price; mixing old pieces with new is a skilled art, therefore keep in mind

the scale and purpose of the items you are sourcing and the period or style you are targeting to ensure you create a truly successful and eclectic interior.

Ros Wilson: When sourcing furniture, fabrics and antiques for your home, do your research. Shop around to gain some knowledge and expertise on the items so that you know what you should be paying for them. Ask questions so that you know what you are purchasing and shop around so that you are in a position to obtain the best price possible.

Above: *Hyde Park Townhouse by SHH – a collaboration of client needs and designers skill*

Design Spotlight: Working together

What do you find is the most successful way of beginning a design relationship with your client? What do you like to hear from them and how can they make the process enjoyable for themselves?

Vincent Kirk: The first face to face meeting is the only way to begin the journey to bring dreams to reality. It is the foundation of the relationship between client and designer - a dialogue which will last for months, sometimes years and over which time we come to learn much about each other: our collective experiences, characters, philosophies; how brave or cautious we both are, our attitudes to risk, and of course our shared visions of the final

design. Our business is getting inside the dreams of our clients.

Susan Knof: For me the most successful way to begin a design relationship with a client is to listen. It's essential to understand what clients are looking for, not only in terms of look and style, but function. I like to start the design process with a visioning session and getting to know the client. This way, I feel I can use my design ethos and approach with their aspirations so that together, we can create a new interior via a collaborative process.

The most resolved designs grow from the sharing of thoughts and ideas.

The best thing I can hear from a client would be, 'Beige is boring, I love colour and I want

to take some risks. Oh, and I hope I didn't forget to mention that my property is located on a picturesque hilltop overlooking the sea in southern Italy!' For any client, my suggestion to make the process enjoyable is to enjoy the journey. Design is a process and part of the fun of the final result is getting there.

Asifa Tirmizi and Scot R.Campbell: I always tell my clients to give me their wish list first, I want them to tell me everything thing they want without thinking about a price tag. I then work backwards on how to incorporate their wish list within the design and also within their budget. Clients that don't have any preconceived ideas for what they want are great for us to work with and a little more exciting, they want us to present what we feel is best for the space. This process is enjoyable for both parties, for us because we have free creative range and for them because they get to see ideas that are brand new to them.

Lindsey Rendall: A relationship between designer and client is fundamental to the success of a project. I always approach a new client with respect, honesty and an open mind and a client should enter the relationship with the same attitude. There is often a perceived arrogance surrounding interior designers, the notion that we are only for the use of the rich and famous and not by 'normal' people, this is not true. An interior designer is an inspirational source and a wealth of knowledge to be utilised, a guide to steer you through your project maximising results to ensure a successful completion whether the project is a large development or the renovation of one awkward small room.

Before I take a client's brief I ask them to produce a board or scrapbook of things which inspires them. Things they love, colours they like, images of important interior items they own and for example a special painting or piece of furniture they want to incorporate into their new scheme. I find this helps my clients formulate their ideas, providing them with something tangible to talk about and it allows me to understand my client within a few minutes rather than drawing information from them in what could feel like an interrogation process!

The most important thing as a client is to be brutally honest with yourself and your designer. Say want you really want to achieve from the project. To save

Above: Rendall and Wright work to the clients desired brief whilst interacting and working their skills into the project

bitter disappointment at the end of a project it's so important to be honest about your taste, budget and time frame at the start; we are not mind readers or magicians! Don't be embarrassed to say you like something no matter how trivial it may feel for it may become the lynchpin for the entire scheme. Two examples which spring to mind are; designing a property following a client producing a handful of Quality Street wrappers and designing a Master Bedroom suite using an antique earring as the sole inspiration.

Armed with your ideas and brief, your interior designer will translate these loose threads of information into a formula and lead you through an exciting process, which will result in a stunning and coherent project. It's a great privilege to design an environment for someone to call home; I involve my clients to ensure I'm representing them throughout and that they enjoy the design process. I want my clients to feel important and integral to the completed design

and consequently that the space belongs to them.

Ros Wilson: A successful start to a client relationship is getting a good grip of your client's personality and adapting to that so that the communication is effortless as without good communication the project is destined to be a struggle. It's always a pleasure when clients are decisive and know what they like / dislike and communicate this to you. As we know this can be a stressful process for a client, so the best approach is to communicate their ideas and trust in the designer's abilities to deliver on what they have communicated.

"It's always a pleasure when clients are decisive and know what they like / dislike and communicate this to you." Ros Wilson

Above: Design by Lucia Caballero – home cinema may become a must-have luxury

Design Spotlight: The Future

What are you most excited about seeing coming out of interior design in 2013?

Vincent Kirk: I would like to see more daring clashes and mixes of colour, pattern and texture, especially using natural fabrics, such as cashmere and silks: materials that not only look good but make you want to engage with them. This tactility is so much more important than homes that look like stage sets but which don't really invite you in on a human level.

Victoria Stainow: I am looking forward to the end of minimalism and soulless interiors. I think people are coming back to fun, warmth, colour and individuality. They are also looking for well

made, often bespoke pieces. As art becomes more important in interior design, so will the design and quality of furniture and lighting. The utilitarian object, when it's beautifully made, can become a work of art.

Susan Knof: In the future I am excited to see how globalisation and incoming international influences can result in evolving design and a new era of reinterpretation - as opposed to imitation. I strongly consider myself a creator not a copier; a designer with original thoughts inspired through a variety of means. I am excited to see how the excessive sharing of ideas and immediacy of the internet can help improve design and how all the other arts - from ballet, film and fashion, to new technology -

can inspire and influence each other in new and inventive ways. On that note, I may need to go and book my next flight to some new foreign and remote land....

Asifa Tirmizi and Scot R.Campbell: We would be excited to see better designs for "off the shelf" interior design products, with all the reality shows these days, it's becoming essential to have better designed products for all those DIY clients.

Lindsey Rendall: The past 15 years have been rather muted and subdued. A largely understated period of neutral colour pallets, plain fabrics, cleans lines, angular shapes and minimal window dressing. Trends are rapidly evolving and what excites me most is the diversity of

Above: Design by Roselind Wilson Design

styles and designs now available across all interior sectors and the ingenious materials being developed for use within the home in kitchens, bathrooms in textiles and as flooring. Whether specifying lighting, furniture, walling, textiles, sanitary wear, AV equipment or appliances the variety of choice is astonishing.

Colour and pattern in textiles are back with vengeance whether to be used for simple block shaded blinds or for heavy traditional embroidered curtains with pelmets. There are fabrics to suit any taste or use and endless ways to bring a collection of styles together either to work with existing schemes or if designing from scratch.

Adorning our walls with fabric, wall panels and wallpaper is also becoming hugely popular instead of simply using paint. Wallpapers with textured designs, huge-scaled bold contemporary prints, delicate, detailed designs and quirky humorous options are extensively available and being utilised throughout rather than reserved for the occasional feature wall.

Lighting and audiovisual schemes are continually developing becoming increasingly sophisticated thus allowing us to integrate them into our designs to create maximum and luxurious effects.

As an industry this change in trend is fantastic as it provides the opportunity for interior designers to be more inventive and experimental with schemes. It allows people to have fun within their homes, to relax and be inspired by the environments they create rather than feeling the need to conform and mould themselves into a style which doesn't reflect who they are.

I think it's safe to say that whatever your preferred design style at the moment you can't go wrong! Dated is great, Chintz is back, sleek and contemporary is effortlessly cool and an eclectic style mix has a retro edge. I foresee 2013 being a year in which confidence grows within design, for people to embrace their interiors and create fantastic and inspiring environments in which to spend their increasingly precious time.

Ros Wilson: With each year, technological advancement results in the most exciting new products and ideas. I'm looking forward to new textures in fabrics and patterns in the designs. Advancement in hard materials for manufacture of furniture will lead to exciting new products that will lend a stamp of originality to interiors as designers are capable of pushing the creative boundaries through the use of new finishes.

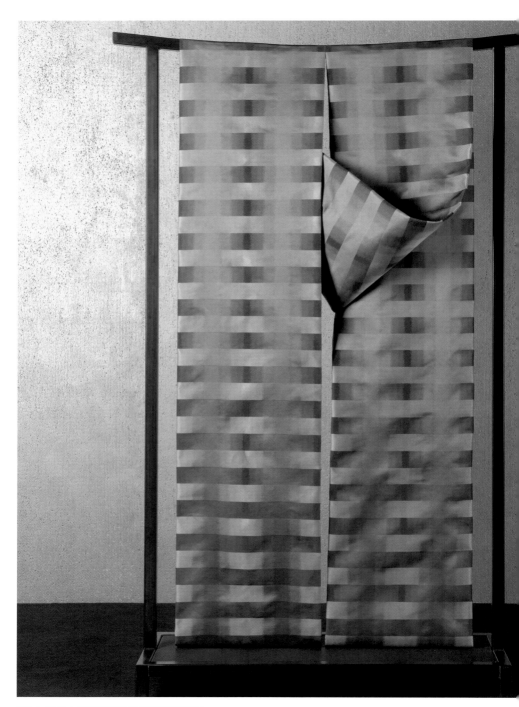

Inspiration boards

The interior design industry has already got a grip on the most prominent trends and designs to hit the design scene in 2013 and beyond. These trends will filter across industries, making their way into the retail sector, presenting you with colours and fabrics that have been carefully considered and thought out to set the tone for design for the next year. There are a multitude of product suppliers that work tirelessly to create the next season's designs to adorn your next scheme. Here, we have gathered together a collection of companies who provide such products to designers and consumers alike, to give a snap shot of some of the colours, fabrics, patterns and designs that will be prominent in 2013.

• RUBELLI VENEZIA •

Bringing an innovative spirit to tradition, suffusing Rubelli's Venetian origins with exoticism, a discreetly colourful and wonderful palette of life illuminates the past with the light of the present.

RRP: From £50.60 per metre
www.rubelli.com

• ORIGINAL BTC •

The Task range comes in a crisp navy blue colour for the season. The lamp is available in table or floor versions. It also comes in polished aluminium, red, olive green, putty, white or black painted aluminium

RRP: £319 (table) £379 (floor)
www.originalbtc.com

• DAVEY LIGHTING •

The traditional box light 'Diner' pendant has now been super-sized to create a robust yet elegant pendant, available in weathered or polished brass and polished or satin nickel.

RRP: From £526.80
www.davey-lighting.co.uk

• DOMINIQUE KIEFFER •

Chinés et Faux Unis expresses a perfect harmony of contrasts, a blend of purity and refinement suspended between period and contemporary. The combination of materials, structures and subtle colours conjure up idyllic country scenes whilst remaining sophisticated and stylish.

RRP: From £71 per metre
www.dominiquekieffer.com

ALEX TURCO AT ANNA CASA •

ex Turco is a contemporary artist. The
ver Kiss, part of the 'Woman Tribute'
lection is featured in the Anna Casa
owroom.

P: On request
w.alexturco.com or www.annacasa.net

• TISSUS D'HÉLÈNE •

The newest designs by Fleurons d'Helene includes Amelie and Eloise and Star Rose, both made with 100% cotton at Tissus d'Hélène.

RRP: On request
www.tissusdhelene.co.uk

• KNOLL STUDIO •

The Krusin Collection is a beautifully crafted range of tables, side and lounge chairs both available with and without arms. The collection is the result of an initial spark of an idea that was then joyously and meticulously re-worked, re-drawn, adjusted and improved until just right.

RRP: On request
www.knoll-int.com

• ILLUMINATI LIGHTING •

The classic design of the Milano pendant is based on an American design by the James Family, re-worked using the finest crystal, it comes in three colour options: Chrome, Champagne, and Gold Crystal; and in a range of sizes.

RRP: On request
www.illuminati-lighting.co.uk

• DONGHIA •

A key asset of the Footloose collection is colour and the changes in light throughout the day; as the light changes, so does the perception of colour. This light-hearted collection, filled with bold patterns and whimsical colours, reflects Donghia's ever evolving and innovative enthusiasm for design.

RRP: From £118 per metre
www.donghia.com

• ARMANI/CASA

EXCLUSIVE TEXTILES BY RUBELLI •

Bringing an innovative spirit to tradition, suffusing Rubelli's Venetian origins with exoticism, a discreetly colourful and wonderful palette of life illuminates the past with the light of the present.

RRP: From £97 per metre
www.rubelli.com

• BAKER •

The Thomas Pheasant Collection by Baker offers a range of furnishings including the new Petal Drum Table. Handcrafted by Baker, the curvaceous form features an organic floral pattern.

RRP: £1296.13 inc. VAT
www.bakerfurniture.com

• TOP FLOOR BY ESTI •

Designed by award-winning designer Esti Barnes, Top Floor presents three new rugs in hand-tufted wool. Using intricate techniques including colour graduation and sculpting, each is a study in surface design.

RRP: ELM (pictured) £784 per sq m
www.topfloorrugs.com

Interior Design:
Appointing an interior designer

By John Evans

Founder, **John Evans Interior Architecture and Design Ltd**

John Evans has been creating classic-contemporary interior design for 30 years. His approach to design is to produce meticulously designed, contemporary-classic interiors. John Evans Interior Architecture and Design specialise in the creation, design and interior architecture of exquisite environments for the commercial, residential and leisure marketplace. John was invited to become a Fellow of the Royal Society for the Arts, as well as being a Member of the Chartered Society of Designers and an active member of the British Institute of Interior Design (BIID). Here, John discusses how professional interior design can help homeowners create the perfect living space.

There are many aspects of a project which can benefit from the assistance of an interior designer; whether it is budgeting, building regulations, or knowing the best suppliers and contractors, interior designers have a diverse knowledge and expertise they can bring to the table of any new-build or home renovation project.

When should you hire an interior designer?

An interior designer should be involved in a project as soon as possible; they should be the first port of call, alongside the architect or builder. Previously, interior designers haven't been given enough credit for the varied knowledge and skills that they possess, but, in fact, designers

Above: Kew Bridge apartments. Designed by Helen Turkington

follow a professional approach and are incredibly well informed, with very strong and useful links to the construction industry.

It's not just style but so much more; knowledge of Building Regulations and the implications for your home, drawing up plans for construction, specifying, ordering goods, space planning, and being able to advise you on the latest and best products and systems on the market.

A designer's speciality is, of course, interiors. Whereas an architect's is generally exteriors and a builder will take a more structural approach to the construction of your home. In contrast, it's the interior designer who will have the better understanding of how the layout or arrangement of a property will affect the interior and, in turn, how this will fit with the lifestyle of its occupants.

As an interior architecture and design practice, we frequently work with architects and other construction professionals. By collaborating together from an early stage, instead of being called in at the end of the building work, we can create a much-improved finished result.

Other benefits for your project

Interior designers can help you from the initial planning stages of a project right through to the end furnishing decisions.

An interior designer's job is to understand their client and create the perfect home to suit their lifestyle; they can take these ideas and make them a reality. Initially, a designer will get to know preferences, tastes, and aspirations for how the homeowner and the family want to live, to put together a structured plan, allowing these

Above: Belgraves Hotel. Designed by Tara Bernerd

tastes to be incorporated in an organised fashion. A designer can also mediate between couples who may have seemingly conflicting views. The interior designer is well placed to negotiate a compromise between the two so that both parties have the home they want.

Interior designers have specialist knowledge of products, systems and building technologies on the market and the best way to use them. With good relationships established with suppliers and contractors, interior designers will know where to source specific products and are again well placed to secure a good deal for the homeowner on price, quality and delivery. With an interior designer on board, the

client can also be confident that the project will also remain within the agreed budget.

From these initial planning stages, the designer will bring these ideas to life through mood boards, sample boards and sketches, enabling the client to see their finished space before the project has even started, allowing for changes to be made before it is too late. They can also construct intricate drawings of proposed plans to enable contractors to provide accurate quotations. At the same time, interior design firms are capable of creating computer-generated walk-through set ups of a potential project.

Throughout the process, the interior designer will be on hand to help with any questions, changes or additional details that may need to be added in, providing a support system right up until the end of the project.

How to find a designer

It is important that you choose a designer that fits your project. There a wide range of designers who have specific skills and expertise, from new-builds to period homes, from living spaces, media rooms and home cinemas to home gyms, spa and pool areas.

A great way of finding the perfect interior designer for your home and your project needs is to look at the British Institute of Interior Design (BIID) website, www.biid.org.uk.

The Institute's website includes profiles of all the BIID members who have passed a rigorous entry process to be listed as a member of the Institute. Homeowners can search through these professional designers, to find one that will fit their project.

The best advice is to then contact a designer and meet them. Don't be shy asking about fee charges and don't limit yourself to local designers; the internet allows designers to work from anywhere in the world and send drawings and information instantly. Many designers are often more than willing to travel. And, if the relationship doesn't feel right, then don't appoint them.

An interior designer has a wide range of skills that can benefit any project. They will be able to look at a space and take into consideration all the factors that determine how it will be used, and create a space that not only meets these needs, but looks fantastic too.

www.johnevansdesign.com

Above: *Courchevel Chalet. Designed by Nico Yiannikou*

www.jessicazoobdesire.com
jessica@jessicazoob.com
07966 572204

I first encountered Jessica's work when I interviewed her for the Sunday Times 'Style' magazine several years ago. I was quite simply blown away by her ability to translate raw emotion and energy onto the canvas, creating whole domains of colour and texture that touch a nerve deep inside our own psyche. Because her work is not constrained by obvious figurative or landscape content, the eye is free to explore the layers within and discover its own worlds - no wonder then that she is the artist of choice for many leading, international interior designers, as her paintings sit as happily in very simple, contemporary interiors as in the lavish and the opulent. Recent projects include foyer and show apartments at The Lancasters, Hyde Park and foyer and premier floors at NEOBankside, Southbank.

Helen Chislett, Journalist & Author.

British Institute of Interior Design
The Institute

Professional designers working towards a creative future

Established in 1966, the BIID is the professional Institute for interior designers in the UK.

The BIID's growing national and international membership represents both the commercial and residential sectors, from heritage to cutting edge. In addition to rigorous entry requirements that assess training, experience and professionalism, the Institute requires members to continue their professional development throughout their career, ensuring their continued expertise in design process, practice and regulatory matters.

The BIID is the only professional organisation for interior designers that has been granted the prestigious and rare accolade of Institute status by the Minister of State as the pre-eminent body in its field. The Institute's mission is to encourage and support creativity and competence in the field of interior design through facilitating best practice, practical professional support, development opportunities and education.

On the national stage, the BIID is a full member of the Construction Industry Council and, as a result, is now part of Government consultations to advise on new policy and legislation. Internationally, the BIID is represented on the board of the International Federation of Interior Architects and Designers; the global voice and authority for professional interior architects and designers.

Council of Directors

The Institute is governed by a Council of elected Directors with relevant skills, expertise or experience for their particular area of responsibility. Council is supported by a carefully constructed Committee structure and most Directors build up their knowledge of the workings of the Institute by serving on one of these committees before joining Council.

President, Sue Timney

Sue is responsible for the strategic development of the Institute. Her key objectives are to work closely with Council, committees and other groups within the design community, nationally and internationally and continue the well-respected work of the Institute as the leading industry body for professional interior designers.

Sue is an influential interior designer who has worked in Britain, Europe and Japan for over 30 years, creating projects that celebrate her own brand of exotic classicism. She is also an Honorary Fellow of the Royal College of Art. Her interior design work covers all aspects of contemporary design, both commercial and residential, in the UK and abroad.

Sue set up the interior design division of Timney-Fowler in 1990, launching Sue Timney Limited in 2002 and the next year opening the Sue Timney showroom at 331 Portobello Road, London. More recently, she was commissioned by The Rug Company in London to design carpets. Sue was also appointed a trustee of The Laura Ashley Foundation and last year The House of Fraser launched the Timney brand for fashion and home. 2011 and 2012 also saw Sue's work represented in the 'Post Modernism 1970-1990' and the 'British Design: Innovation in the Modern Age' exhibitions at the Victoria and Albert Museum in London.

Past President, Diana Yakeley

As Past President, Diana continues to work on the strategic development of the Institute as well as providing the Council with experienced advice by liaising with the Audit Committee and Past President's club. Diana has written books on design, as well as professional practice and contracts.

Operations and Finance Director, Patti Money Coutts

Patti's key aims are to continue strengthening existing management reporting and control procedures to enable Council and executive staff to plan and monitor costs and income on a timely basis. She is responsible for developing staff and office procedures, IT and premises in addition to helping to provide a sound basis for the current and planned growth of the Institute. Patti runs her own interior design practice based in Hampshire.

Membership Director, Brian Lawrence

Brian's aims are to continue the growth in the institute membership in all categories with the continuing support of its strong and experienced committee. He has been a designer member of the organisation for many years and runs his own fabric, wallpaper and custom design business.

Heritage and Environment Director, Christopher Vane Percy

Christopher works to further the Institute's work in the fields of heritage and the environment. He is an established interior designer, Regional Chairman of the Historic Houses Association for East Anglia Region and is a committee member of the East of England Historic Environment Forum.

International Director, Simon Hamilton

Simon's recent travels to Japan, France, Australia, USA and UAE, have been to promote the benefits of using creative and highly trained British Designers. By seeking new opportunities and potential collaborations with practices abroad, this will help UK based interior designers who wish to reach a global market. He is already busy organizing Trade Missions to the USA for this year with other destinations under consideration. With over 20 years in the industry, Simon runs his own interior design company serving commercial and high-end residential clients.

Associate and Student Director, Hayley Manning

Hayley's key aims are to provide support, organise events and encourage networking for Student and Associate members of the Institute. Hayley runs her own interior design practice based in London.

CPD Director, Dan Hopwood

Dan oversees the Institute's CPD programme of seminars, lectures and tours in addition to the expansion of its CPD Providers Directory. Dan trained as an architect and now runs his own interior design practice based in London and France.

Marketing Director, Debra McQuin

Debra oversees the Institute's overall marketing strategy. Debra has a background in marketing and communications and now runs her own residential interior design practice based in London.

Education Director, Helen Keighley

Helen is responsible for the development of the Institute's soon to be launched Professional Pathway and for building relationships between colleges and universities and the Institute. Helen is the Director of Quality and Business at the National Design Academy.

Industry Partner Director, David Graham

Industry Partner Director, David, serves as the voice for industry partner members, heading up the BIID's Industry Partner committee. David brings a wealth of relevant experience to his role representing Industry Partner members on Council. He is Managing Director of Grahams Hi-Fi and has worked with membership organisation the Custom and Electronics Design and Installation Association (CEDIA) as a volunteer; serving as a chairman and has also acted as the trade body's Outreach Chair.

www.biid.org.uk.

Above: *The BIID are situated at the Design Centre Chelsea Harbour*

British Institute of Interior Design

The Membership

Find an interior design professional or practice

Mrs. Ruth Ackers
in and out design
www.inandoutdesign.co.uk
01702 340272

Mr. David Ackers
David Ackers Design Associates
www.davidackers.com
33 233 947400

Mr. Alidad
Alidad Limited
www.alidad.com
020 7384 0121

Mr. Mohammed Abu Aljadayel
Eclectic Interiors
www.empire-m.com
00 9662 6072992

Mr. Jon Wilson Allen
Entasis Architecture
www.entasis.bm
+441 292 6629

Mr. John Amabile
Amabile Design Ltd
www.amabiledesign.com
0845 4502601

Mrs. Fiona Andrews
Fiona Andrews Interiors Limited
www.fionaandrewsinteriors.com
020 7610 9119

Mrs. Harriet Anstruther
Harriet Anstruther Studio Ltd
www.harrietanstruther.com
020 7584 4776

Mrs. Fiona Applegarth
Sable Interiors
www.sableinteriors.com
020 8398 9777

Countess Monika Apponyi
MM Design
www.biid.org.uk
020 7751 0171

Mr. Ian Ashworth
i-lid Design
www.i-lid.co.uk
01733 396181

Mrs. Angela Aston
Trineire Designs
www.trineire.com
020 8297 4144

Mr. Doug Atherley
Kinari Design Ltd
www.kinaridesign.com
020 7221 9569

Mrs. Christy Austin
Austin Interior Design
www.austindesign.co.uk
020 7581 4551

Mr. Emile Azan
Chameleon Designs
www.chameleondesigns.org
020 8473 1363

Ms. Diana Bailey
Bailey Lewis
www.biid.org.uk
01621 782002

Mrs. Beverley Barnett
Beverley Barnett
www.beverleybarnett.co.uk
01923 857029

Ms. Kathleen Barron
Barron Design
www.barrondesign.co.uk
01425 471233

Miss Deborah Bass
Base interior
www.baseinterior.com
020 7486 5690

Ms. Ingrid Batcup
I B Design
www.renoir-interiors.co.uk
01792 386766

Ms. Lucinda Batt
Lucinda Batt Interior Design
Consultant
www.theinteriorlibrary.ie
+35 3169 1908

Ms. Lizzie Bell
Lizzie Bell Interiors Ltd
www.biid.org.uk
0131 555 6855

Mr. Bill Bennette
Bill Bennette Design Limited
www.bbdesign.co.uk
020 7351 2550

Mr. John Beven
Wilkinson Beven Design Ltd
www.wilkinsonbevendesign.com
0121 744 1458

Mr. Matteo Bianchi
Matteo Bianchi Studio
www.matteobianchi.co.uk
0207 275 7774

Ms. Kate Bingham
Kate Bingham Interior Design Ltd
www.kbidesign.co.uk
01798 860999

Mr. Mark Bithrey
B3 Designers Ltd
www.b3designers.co.uk
020 7729 8111

Mrs. Jenny Blanc
Jenny Blanc
www.jennyblanc.com
020 8943 4440

Ms. Melanie Boissevain
Melanie Boissevain
www.melanieboissevain.com
01646 661787

Ms. Jane Bower
Bower Mapson
www.bowermapson.co.uk
01865 750417

Mr. Ben Bracey
Bracey Interiors
www.biid.org.uk
01179 239919

Ms. Louise Bradley
Louise Bradley
www.louisebradley.co.uk
020 7589 1442

Mr. Pierre Brahm
Brahm Interiors
www.brahminteriors.com
020 7235 3333

Mrs. Jessica Brook
Jessica Brook Design
www.jessicabrookdesign.com
020 7731 8745

Mr. Jonathan Brunskill
Jonathan Brunskill Associates
www.jonathanbrunskill.co.uk
020 8995 5645

Ms. Philippa Buckley
Studio 44 Design
www.studio44.ie
+353 1296 4208

Mrs. Helen Bygraves
Hill House Interiors
www.hillhouseinteriors.com
01932 858900

Ms. Juliette Byrne
Juliette Byrne Ltd
www.juliettebyrne.com
020 7352 1553

Mr. Louis Calleja
John Nash Antiques & Interiors
www.johnnash.co.uk
01531 635714

Miss Katrina Callow
Foreign & Commnwealth Office
www.estategroup.co.uk
2070081400

Ms. Ruth Canning
Canning & Sheridan Interiors.
www.canning-sherdian.co.uk
020 7232 2660

Ms. Audrey Carden
Carden Cunietti Ltd
www.carden-cunietti.com
020 7724 9679

Mr. Eduardo Cardenes
Cardenes Studio Ltd
www.cardenesstudio.com
2074600341

Mr. Robert Carslaw
Robert Carslaw Design
www.robertcarslaw.com
020 7376 4440

Mr. Matthew Chamberlain
Design ACB LTD
www.designacb.com
01256 414450

Ms. Gilly Chance
Stavedene Ltd
www.stavedenedesigns.co.uk
020 7407 4313

Ms. Angie Charteris
Hamble Interiors Ltd
www.biid.org.uk
01491 577 987

Mr. Benjamin Clarke
Curve Interior Design Ltd
www.curveinteriordesign.co.uk
0161 237 9300

Ms. Clarissa Clifford
Clarissa Clifford
www.biid.org.uk
01626 853655

Mr. Howard Clulow
M J Barrett
www.barrettgroup.co.uk
01889 564295

Mrs. Angela Cook
Christopher Cook Designs Ltd
www.christophercook.co.uk
020 8941 9135

Mrs. Caroline Cooper
Caroline Cooper Interiors
www.carolinecooper.co.uk
020 8297 9278

Mrs. Sara Corker
Sara Corker Designs
www.saracorkerdesigns.com
01342 894613

Mr. Michael Costley-White
MCW Associates
www.mcw-associates.com
1285831757

Mrs. Pamela Cox
Ham Interiors Ltd
www.haminteriors.com
01491 579 371

Mrs. Gilly Craft
Koubou Interiors
www.koubouinteriors.co.uk
01344 779323

Mrs. Looby Crean
Looby Crean Ltd
www.BIID.org.uk
020 8742 2333

Ms. Eleanora Cunietti
Carden Cunietti Ltd
www.carden-cunietti.com
020 7724 9679

Mrs. Sue Dann
Sue Dann Interiors
www.suedanninteriors.com
01628 488 521

Mrs. Lavinia Dargie
Dargie Lewis Designs
www.dargielewis.com
020 7736 6840

Mr. Rene Dekker
Rene Dekker Design Limited
www.renedekker.co.uk
020 7036 1699

Ms. Elisabeth Denny
Margaret Sheridan Interior
Decoration and Design
www.margaretsheridan.co.uk
01953 850691

Ms. Sally Dernie
Sally Dernie Limited
www.sallydernie.com
020 7738 1628

Oro Bianco Interior Design
www.orobiancointeriordesign.com
020 7591 1920

Mrs. Philippa Devas
Devas Designs
www.devasdesigns.co.uk
0207 584 9966

Mr. Christopher Dezille
Honky Design Ltd
www.honky.co.uk
020 7622 7144

Mr. Stephen Dick
Residence Interior Design
www.residenceinteriordesign.com
01730 829 566

Ms. Jane Dodson
KSD Design Company
www.ksd-design.co.uk
01962 760 353

Mrs. Suzy Donaldson
Suzy Dallas Limited
www.suzydallas.com
01725 519685

Mr. Paul Douglas
Room
www.roomid.co.uk
07947 187 053

Ms. Iris Dunbar
The Interior Design School
www.theinteriordesignschool.co.uk
2073722811

Ms. Jacqueline Duncan
Inchbald School of Design
www.inchbald.co.uk
020 7630 9011

Ms. Janet Eavenson
Leonard Provence Interiors
www.leanoardprovenceinteriors.com
2076103189

Ms. kitty Edwards-Jones
Kitty-lynne Jones Interior Design
www.kitty-lynnejonesinteriordesign.com
07973 755095

Ms. Willa Elphinstone
Drumkilbo Designs
www.biid.org.uk
01620 861400

Ms. Leila Corbett Elwes
Leila Corbett Limited
www.leila-corbett.com
020 7349 0000

Mr. John Evans
John Evans Interiors Ltd
www.johnevansdesign.com
0121 233 9041

Mr. Jonathan Everitt
Orium Design Limited
www.oriumdesign.co.uk
01905 797501

Ms. Zeynep Fadillioglu
MF Turistik Tesisleri Isletme ve
Tasarim Dekorasyon Tic A.S
www.zfdesign.com
+90 212 2870936

Mrs. Marion Falchi-Pereira
Falchi Interiors Limited
www.falchiinteriors.com
01753 540890

Ms. Christina Fallah
Christina Fallah Designs Limited
www.christina-fallah-designs.com
0207 584 1240

Ms. Fiona Finlay
Fiona S. Finlay
www.fionasfinlay.com
01887 840 488

Ms. Sue Fisher
Fisher ID
www.fisherid.com
01689 896 227

Mrs. Jacqueline Fisken
Ampersand
www.ampersandinteriors.co.uk
0131 557 6634

Casa Forma
www.casaforma.co.uk
020 7584 9495

Ms. Mary Barber Fray
Mary Barber Fray Interior Design
www.marybarberfray.co.uk
0121 445 0326

Ms. Roberta Fulford
Roberta Fulford
www.robertafulford.com
01422 825130

Ms. Nobuko Furuichi
Thirty Three Co., Ltd
www.organizer.jp
06-4803-0100

Ms. Cynthia Garcia
Garcia Designs
www.garciadesigns.co.uk
020 8877 3863

Mr. Darren Gayer
The Sheldon Studio Ltd
www.thesheldonstudio.com
020 8446 4466

Mrs. Kate Gedye
Acanthus Clews Architects
www.acanthusclews.co.uk
01295 702600

Ms. Debbie Gee
DG Interiors
www.dginteriors.co.uk
020 8274 8921

Ms. Junko Gennami
JG INTERNATIONAL CONSULTING
LIMITED
www.livingbydesign.jp
+852 9867 0415

Mrs. Pamela George
George Interiors Ltd
www.georgeinteriors.co.uk
01746 767441

Mrs. Jennifer Gibbs
KLC
www.klc.co.uk
020 7376 3377

Mrs. Brenda Gibson
Complete Interior Co. Ltd
www.completeinterior.co.uk
020 8878 2282

Mr. Mark Gillette
Mark Gillette Interior Design Ltd
www.markgillette.com
01244 851897

Mrs. Bridget Glasgow
Bridget Glasgow Interior Design
www.bridgetglasgow.com
01725 518500

Mr. Matthew Godley
MGID Ltd
www.matthewgodley.co.uk
020 8968 1306

Mr. Tim Gosling
Gosling Ltd
www.tgosling.com
020 7498 8335

Mrs. Katy Graham
Interior Being Ltd
www.interiorbeing.com
020 7407 4899

Mrs. Odile Granter
Granter Interiors
www.granterinteriors.com
020 7835 0671

Mrs. Jennifer Granville-Dixon
Granville-Dixon Designs
www.biid.org.uk
020 7731 0139

Mr. Veere Grenney
Veere Grenney Associates
www.veeregrenney.com
020 7351 7170

The Palladian Group
www.palladiangroup.co.uk
020 7371 2100

Mr. David Hales
David Hales Interior Design Ltd
www.davidhalesinteriordesign.co.uk
01372 750290

Ms. Annabel Hall
Private Lives
www.privatelives.co.uk
01252 850527

Mrs. Louise Hart
Atkins Limited
www.atkinsglobal.com
01392 352958

Mr. Roland Hartmann
Hartmann designs Ltd
www.hartmanndesigns.com
020 8694 6915

Mrs. Anne Hatton
Embellishments Ltd
www.embellishmentsltd.com
01753 882425

Mr. Robert von Hawrylak
Felbrigg Design Company Ltd
www.felbriggdesign.com
01249 720076

Ms. Genny Henderson
The Room Company
www.theroomcompany.com
020 7262 9107

Ms. Catherine Henderson
Catherine Henderson Design
www.catherinehenderson.com
0141 423 4321

Mrs. Diana Henshall
Di Henshall Interior Design
www.dihenshall.com.au
+61 75449 0788

Ms. Colette Hoepli-Steffan
Steffan Interiors Ltd
www.steffaninteriors.com
020 8209 0647

Ms. Anja Hoffmann
Anja Hoffmann Project
Management & Interiors
www.anja-hoffmann.com
+34 96 579 63 26

Mrs. Louise Holt
Cloud Studios
www.cloudstudios.co.uk
01865 343526

Ms. Kelly Hoppen
Kelly Hoppen Interiors
www.kellyhoppen.com
020 7471 3350

Mr. Daniel Hopwood
DanielHopwood.com
www.danielhopwood.com
020 7286 2004

Mrs. Frances Horn
FHI Design.com
www.fhidesign.com
01264 333 642

Mr. Khalid Al Hubail
Nattily Co.
www.nattily.com
+966 3 58407707

Ms. Tanya Hudson
Amok Ltd
www.amok.co.uk
020 7993 4447

Ms. Niki Hudson
Hudson Designers Ltd
www.hudsondesigners.com
020 7112 4992

Ms. Penelope Hughes-Ross
CAPSTONE
www.capstoneinteriordesign.com
0208 747 1333

Miss Lynne Hunt
Lynne Hunt London
www.lynnehunt.co.uk
020 7581 6601

Godrich Interiors
www.godrichinteriors.com
0207 229 3966

AS Interiors
www.as-interiors.com
00973 17716639

Mr. Bruce Irwin
Bruce Irwin Studio
www.bruceirwin.co.uk
020 7820 7693

Mr. Hugh Jamieson
At Home
www.athome-interiors.com
01223 832429

Ms. Samantha Johnson
Samantha Johnson Interior Design
www.samanthajohnsondesign.com
01628 532 517

Ms. Sylvia Lawson Johnston
Sylvia Lawson Johnston Interior
Design
www.biid.org.uk
01975 651402

Mrs. Janet Jones
Partners Interiors
www.partnersinteriors.co.uk
020 8458 2922

Mrs. Leanne Jones
Atkins Limited
www.atkinsglobal.com
01392 352900

Ms. Debra Kacher
dk Interiors
www.dkinteriors.uk.com
020 8455 1254

Ms. Junko Kamei
Juju Interior Designs Ltd
www.tc-juju.com
+81 561 58 1061

Mrs. Mia Karlsson-Matthews
Mia Karlsson Interior Design
www.miakarlsson.co.uk
020 72091615

Mrs. Michelle Kauffmann
MK Interior Design
www.mkinteriordesign.com
07787 833506

Mrs. Louisa Keating
Atlantic Interior Design Ltd
www.atlanticinteriordesign.com
020 7243 6364

Mr. Anthony Keenor
Interior Enterprises Ltd
www.interiorenterprises.co.uk
020 8763 8422

Ms. Tessa Kennedy
Tessa Kennedy Design
www.tessakennedydesign.com
020 7221 4546

Ms. Julie Kent
Julie Kent Interiors
www.juliekentinteriors.com
01249 715222

Ms. Eleonora Kessler
Quintessence interior design
www.quintessence.co.at
0043 664477 5496

Mr. Dean Keyworth
Armstrong Keyworth
www.armstrong-keyworth.co.uk
020 7352 0539

Mrs. Rachael Kilby-Tyre
Absolute Designs Ltd
www.absolute-designs.eu
01242 580884

Ms. Susan Knof
SHH
www.shh.co.uk
020 8600 4171

Mr. Hansjurgen Laade
Home Interieur Design
www.laade-design.de
+49 02132 5714

Ms. Niloufar Lamakan
Nila Design
www.niladesign.co.uk
020 7697 4600

Mrs. Carole Langton
Langton Interiors
www.langtoninteriors.co.uk
020 7376 3600

Ms. Heidi Larson
Larson Design
www.heidilarsondesign.com
32 2 772 07 44

Mr. Brian Lawrence
Brian Lawrence Ltd
www.brianlawrence.net
01732 741308

Ms. Caroline Lawson
Chelsea Decorators
www.chelseadecorators.com
01939 261122

Ms. Alexandra Lawson
Lawson Robb Associates Ltd
www.lawsonrobb.com
020 7351 9383

Mrs. Rachel Laxer
Rachel Laxer Interiors Ltd
www.rlaxerinteriors.com
020 7624 0738

Miss Mary Leslie
MARY LESLIE INTERIOR DESIGN
www.mhleslie.co.uk
020 8675 0910

Mr. Hugh Leslie
Hugh Leslie Design LLP
www.hughleslie.com
020 7584 7185

Ms. Christine May Lewsey
Christine May Interior Design
www.christinemayinteriors.co.uk
020 8498 0950

Taylor Howes Designs Limited
www.taylorhowes.co.uk
020 7349 9017

Shalini Misra Limited
www.shalinimisra.com
020 7266 6181

Antonia Stewart Limited
www.antoniastewart.com
020 7386 0110

Ms. Ina Lindemann
Ina Lindemann Interior Design Ltd
www.inalindemann.co.uk
020 7373 7783

Mr. Gordon Lindsay
Gordon Lindsay Design Limited
www.gordonlindsay.co.uk
01379 586799

Mrs. Mary Fox Linton
Fox Linton Associates
www.foxlinton.co.uk
020 7907 2269

Ms. Susan Llewellyn
Susan Llewellyn Associates
www.susanllewellynassociates.com
0208 563 1555

Tessuto Interiors Ltd
www.tessuto.co.uk
020 7371 0117

Blanchard Ltd
www.blanchard.uk.com
020 7722 1242

Think Design (Leeds) Ltd
www.thinkdesignleeds.co.uk
01943 604448

The Studio Harrods Ltd
www.thestudioatharrods.com
020 7225 5926

Boscolo Ltd
www.boscolo.co.uk
0845 2020208

Mr. John Lusk
Mrs Monro Ltd
design@mrsmonro.co.uk
0844 984 1524

Mr. Douglas Mackie
D Mackie Design Ltd.
www.dmackiedesign.com
020 7487 3295

Mrs. Giselle Mannering
de hasse
www.dehasse.co.uk
01732 457008

Ms. Gail Marsden
Gail Marsden Design
www.gailmarsdendesign.co.uk
0161 439 2197

Mr. John McCall
John McCall Ltd
www.mccalldesign.co.uk
01635 578007

Ms. Katie McCrum
London Rooms Design Ltd
www.londonroomsdesign.com
0776 7473444

Miss Joanne McDonald
Luma Interiors
www.luma-interiors.co.uk
0131 331 3726

Ms. Tina McFarlane
Hard Design & Management Ltd
www.tmcfdesigns.co.uk
0207 223 4626

Miss Karen McKimmie
Ambiance Interior Design
www.ambiance.co.uk
01224 310 211

Mrs. Diana McKnight
KLC School of Design
www.klc.co.uk
020 7376 7400

Mr. Paul McNulty
Foreign & Commonwealth Office
fcoservices.gov.uk
020 7008 1387

Mrs. Debra McQuin
McQuin Partnership
www.mcquinpartnership.com
7799690826

Ms. Davina Merola
Space Alchemy Ltd
www.space-alchemy.com
020 7987 1622

Mr. Socrates Miltiadou
Richard Mitzman Architects
www.richardmitzman.com
020 8348 8411

Mr. Fadi Mneimneh
TAO Designs L.L.C.
www.taouae.com
+9714 2271633

Mr. Mehdi Moazzen
Point of Design LLC
www.poddubai.com
00971 433 66 151

Mrs. Patti Money-Coutts
Overbury Interiors
www.overburyinteriors.co.uk
01420 590219

Ms. Siobhan Mooney
Siobhan Mooney Interior Design
www.roomid.co.uk
0131 554 5500

Mrs. Geraldine Morley
GERALDINE MORLEY INTERIOR
DESIGN Ltd
www.geraldinemorley.com
020 8341 3608

Ms. Nia Morris
Cloud Studios
www.cloudstudios.co.uk
2075865670

Ms. Shiro Muchiri
Interni Design Studio
www.internidesignstudio.com
020 8969 3241

Miss Nicky Mudie
Violet & George
www.violetandgeorge.com
020 8969 0654

Mr. Akiho Murakami
Akiho Murakami Design Consultant
www.biid.org.uk
020 8332 2752

Ms. Carolyne Myers
Caz Myers Design
www.cazmyers.com
020 8348 6464

Mrs. Cecilia Neal
Meltons
www.meltons.co.uk
020 7233 9712

Ms. Claire Nelson
Nelson Design Ltd
www.nelsondesign.co.uk
020 7935 8600

Ms. Melanie Nelson
Addison Nelson UK
www.addisonnelson.com
020 8749 7627

Mrs. Iona Newton
Oakeve Limited
www.oakeve.com
01494 737461

Mrs. Jennifer Nicholas
The Design Buro Ltd.
www.designburo-architects.co.uk
01788 555350

Mr. Michael Nicholas
Michael Nicholas Design
www.michaelnicholasdesign.com
020 7498 7755

Ms. Jane O'Connor
IOR Group Ltd
www.iorgroup.co.uk
020 8614 9500

Mr. Toshinori Okino
ILYA Corporation
www.ilya.co.jp
81 (0)3 5561 1533

Mr. Guy Oliver
Oliver Laws Limited
www.oliverlaws.com
020 7437 8487

Mr. Colin Orchard
Colin Orchard and Company Ltd.
www.biid.org.uk
0207 351 5501

Mr. Anthony Paine
Anthony Paine Limited
www.anthonypaine.com
01225 331935

Mrs. Caroline Palk
Ashton House Design
www.ashtonhousedesign.co.uk
01364 653563

Ms. Gloria de Palleja
Gloria de Palleja Design & Interior
Architecture
www.gpalleja.com
+933 195 763

Ms. Carolyn Parker
Carolyn Parker Interior Design
www.carolynparker.com
01347 878 820

Mrs. Clare Pascoe
Pascoe Interiors Ltd
www.pascoeinterios.com
01243 785 100

Mrs. Rina Patel
Vastu Design
www.vastu.co.uk
020 8813 2985

Mr. Steven Payne
Maison Architecure & Design Ltd
www.maisonad.com
+44 (0) 7720914413

Mr. Maurizio Pellizzoni
Maurizio Pellizzoni Design Limited
www.mpdlondon.co.uk
020 7025 8013

Mr. Christopher Vane Percy
CVP Designs Limited
www.cvpdesigns.com
020 8960 9026

Mr. Daniel Perez-Selsky
ASTAD
www.biid.org.uk
+974 4130366/413 0803

Mr. Gregory Phillips
Gregory Phillips Interiors
www.gregoryphillips.com
020 7724 3040

Mr. Alfred Mok Wa Ping
Alfred Mok Designs Ltd
www.alfredmokdesigns.com
+852 5775501

Mrs. Lori Pinkerton-Rolet
Park Grove Design
www.parkgrove.co.uk
020 8969 0110

Ms. Katharine Pooley
Katharine Pooley Limited
www.katharinepooley.com
0207 584 3223

Ms. Susan Quirke
Quirke McNamara Consultancy LLP
www.q-mc.co.uk
0208 5670609

Mrs. Chanelle Rains
Gramlick Designs Ltd
www.gramlickdesigns.co.uk
1608664563

Mrs. Francie Readman
Francie Readman Interiors
www.franciereadmaninteriors.com
01255 861507

Mrs. Lindsey Rendall
Rendall & Wright
www.rendallandwright.com
7971487899

Ms. Michelle Reyes-Gerber
Kre8if Designs
www.kre8ifdesigns.com
+41 55 210 1426

Ms. Charlotte Robb
Lawson Robb Associates Ltd
www.lawsonrobb.com
020 7351 9383

Mrs. Carole Roberts
No. Twelve Queen Street Ltd.
www.twelvedesign.co.uk
01225 462363

Ms. Julia Roberts
Vivette Maison Design
www.vivettemaisondesign.com
01929 558120

Ms. Gillian Rogerson
Gillian Rogerson Design Ltd
www.gillianrogerson.co.uk
020 7917 9594

Ms. April Russell
April russell Designs Ltd
www.aprilrussell.com
2030550090

Ms. Katharine Rutherford
Gramlick Designs
www.gramlickdesigns.co.uk
01608 664573

Mr. STEPHEN RYAN
Stephen Ryan Design & Decoration
www.stephenryandesign.com
020 7243 0864

Mrs. Eliska Sapera
Eliska Design Associates Ltd
www.eliskadesign.com
020 7723 5521

Ms. Noriko Sawayama
Noriko Sawayama Design &
Associates Ltd
www.nsda-uk.com
020 3178 2188

Miss Jill Scholes
Jill Scholes Interior Design
www.jillscholes.co.uk
020 8969 7001

Mrs. Omeima Osman Sid-Ahmed
www.biid.org.uk
+974 4311524

Mr. John Smith
Individual Interior Design
www.individualinteriordesign.co.uk
01202 763256

Mr. Ian Smith
Ian Smith Design Ltd
www.iansmithdesign.co.uk
0131 332 2500

Mrs. Ann Spencer
Country House Interiors & Lighting
www.chillinteriors.co.uk
01435 830608

Lady Henrietta Spencer-Churchill
Woodstock Designs
www.spencerchurchilldesigns.com
020 7731 8399

Ms. Jane Spencer-Churchill
Jane Churchill Interiors Ltd.
www.janechurchillinteriors.com
020 7730 8564

Mr. Nico Springman
Inchbald School of Design
www.inchbald.co.uk
020 7730 5508

Ms. Beverley Spyer-Holmes
Beverley Hills Interiors
www.beverleyhillsinteriors.co.uk
01438 840017

Miss Donna Staples
Pellings LLP
www.pellings.co.uk
020 8460 9114

Mr. Oliver Steer
Oliver Steer: Interior Designers and
Architects
www.oliversteer.com
0207 969 1802

Mrs. Annie Stevens
Annie Stevens Designs Ltd
www.anniestevens.co.uk
020 8874 1393

Mrs. Marie-Noelle Swiderski
Blanchard FZ LLC
www.blanchard.uk.com
+ 971 4369 4532

Mrs. Jacqueline Tate
Hafod Fabrics Ltd
www.hafodfabrics.com
01981 540 367

Ms. Juliet Taylor
Juliet Taylor Design Ltd
www.biid.org.uk
01736 351 589

Mrs. Lesley Taylor
Taylor's Etc Design Ltd
www.taylorsetc.co.uk
029 20358400

Kay Pilsbury Thomas
www.kpt.co.uk
01799 599208

Ms. Philippa Thorp
Philippa Thorp Design Limited
www.thorp.co.uk
020 7731 6887

Mr. Neil Trett
Hazle McCormack Young LLP
www.hmy.uk.com
01227 454497

Mrs. Jennifer Truman
Limited Editions Interior Design
Consultants
www.limitededitionscom.co.uk
01903 744270

Mrs. Marcia Tucker
Marcia Tucker Interiors LLC
www.marciatuckerinteriors.com
1-203 409 3692

Ms. Suzanne Tucker
Suzanne Tucker Interiors
www.suzannetucker-interiors.com
01306 884148

Mrs. Claire Tull
Studio12 Designs
www.s12d.co.uk
0118 941 8203

Miss Bunny Turner
Turner Pocock
www.turnerpocock.co.uk
020 34632390

Mrs. Julia Twigg
Julia Twigg (PTY) Ltd
www.biid.org.uk
+27 11 884 3539

Ms. Karin Verzariu
Key Interiors
www.keyinteriors.com
445601267291

Mr. Ian Walton
Ian Walton Associates
www.biid.org.uk
07774 776083

Ms. Min Wang
Shenzhen 2TY Design Group Co.,
Ltd
www.wminart.com
+86 755 222 74201

Mrs. Sarah Ward
Sarah Ward Associates Ltd
www.sarahwardassociates.com
08445 611876

Ms. Alice Webster
alice webster interiors limited
www.burchell-interiors.com
020 8368 8982

Mrs. Jenny Weiss
Hill House Interiors
www.hillhouseinteriors.com
01932 858 900

Mr. David Wells
Aura Designworks Ltd
www.auradesignworks.co.uk
01442 500 070

Mrs. Karen White
Source Interiors Ltd.
www.biid.org.uk
020 7243 1488

Ms. Marianna Wilford
Marianna Wilford Interiors Limited
www.biid.org.uk
+44 207 751 5757

Mr. Richard Wilkinson
Wilkinson Beven Design
www.wilkinsonbevendesign.com
0121 744 1458

Ms. Rosie Winston
Clifton Interiors
www.cliftoninteriors.com
020 7586 5533

Mrs. Sarah Wodehouse
Decibel Designs
www.decibeldesigns.co.uk
020 7821 9491

Mrs. Sarah Wodehouse
Decibel Designs
www.decibeldesigns.co.uk
020 7821 9491

Ms. Joanna Wood
Joanna Trading Ltd
www.joannatrading.com
020 7730 0693

Mr. William Woods
Woods of Harrogate Ltd
www.woodsofharrogate.com
01423 530111

Mrs. Alison Wright
Future Proof Home Ltd t/as Easy
Living Home
www.easylivinghome.co.uk
01844 273003

Mrs. Melissa Wyndham
Melissa Wyndham Limited
www.melissawyndham.com
020 7352 2874

Mrs. Diana Yakeley
Yakeley Associates Ltd
www.yakeley.com
020 7609 9846

Mr. York Yao
York Design Studio
www.biid.org.uk
07988 558 919

Interior Design:
Design Education

By Jacqueline Duncan and Alan Hughes
Principal and Vice Principal,
Inchbald School of Design

The Inchbald School of Design, based in London, is an independent school of interior design, interior decoration and garden design. The School has a long-established reputation for serious, practical training that is designed to prepare our graduates to enter the design professions and has a proven record in terms of graduate achievement within each discipline. Jacqueline Duncan founded the Inchbald School of Interior Design in 1960, extending this to a Faculty in Garden Design in 1972. Her previous working experience included the management of the Michael Inchbald Studios, antique dealing also under the Inchbald banner, and colour consultancy work. Alan obtained a degree in Visual Communications at Brighton School of Art and has practised as a graphic designer and illustrator, working for a number of leading magazines and publishing houses. His teaching experience includes five years at Middlesex University after which he joined Inchbald in 1991. After a period as Director of Visual Communication he took over the Directorship of the Architectural Interior Design Faculty and in 2002 he was appointed Vice Principal of the college.

There is still a perception that finding work in a design firm provides an inexpensive shortcut into the design profession and this may of course be equated with the apprenticeship system, which certainly provided excellent training in the past.

However in the climate that pertains today, with ever more demanding technology proceeding faster than we can think, that rather leisurely approach to professional training cannot provide a substitute for carefully conceived and disciplined education, culminating in recognised qualifications.

In order to preserve and support the status of the interior design profession it is increasingly

Above: *"The main function of any educational programme is to instruct the student in the fundamental knowledge required to implement their chosen career."*

essential that practitioners acknowledge the importance of qualifications which are there, not only for the enhancement of student knowledge and ambition, but also for the protection of future clients.

The main function of any educational programme is to instruct the student in the fundamental knowledge required to implement their chosen career. Throughout such a course design students should learn to analyse not only the brief but the characteristics of the client as well, exploring their own ideas and at the same time exercising the discipline endemic to any profession. The nature of design is about innovative thinking; a successful educational environment must encourage and promote individual talent but must also ensure that the student is fully informed about construction and material, crafts and styles, all of which are vital to the implementation of their talents.

The multi-disciplinary world of interior design requires an informed balance of practical, aesthetic and theoretical knowledge; and any educational programme that aims to produce professionally relevant alumni must take care to produce such a balance.

Today the standards in UK design have benefited immeasurably from the improvement in those centres dedicated to the specifics of design in Higher Education. 21st Century practices employing new graduates want to see the skills with which we are all familiar. But in addition they are looking for cutting edge inspiration and analytical facilities, both in the consultation rooms and on the drawing board.

A good design education

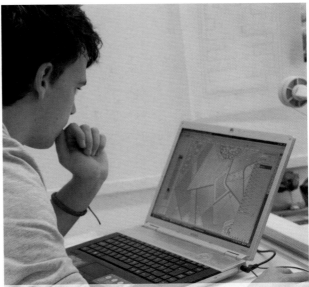

Above: "As educators we are here to launch new and proficient designers into the world of design business, making it possible for them to show what they are capable of."

must provide an atmosphere where all this is possible. In addition it must provide a well established connection to the professional world, arranging internships as part of the experience and offering career advice for as long as alumni need it.

As educators we are here to launch new and proficient designers into the world of design business, making it possible for them to show what they are capable of, not only now but in the bright future.

So today there is no short cut to being a successful practitioner in the design world. However possible this may have been in a more leisurely past, it is a system, which cannot encompass the demands of the 21st century. Students need now to consider their options with the greatest care and weigh up the advantages that are endemic in

formal education. Above all they should be aware of the breadth of opportunity that exists in their chosen field.

Every potential designer requires an environment that suits their creative patterns, that will provide them with all the appropriate core skills and at the same time encourage and inform in a manner designed to develop exceptional talents and individuality. These are the considerations that must be taken into account when the would-be designer considers not only the quality of education but also the characteristics of the singular profession to which he or she aspires.

Unquestionably it is wise to take the structured way into your future and give it your total commitment.

www.inchbald.co.uk

OFFtheWALL

Audio Visual Furniture Collection

At **Off the Wall** we design and manufacture a stunning range of audio visual furniture that fits beautifully into any interior. Our inovitive furniture hides all the clutter of cables and wires and is available in a large selection of finishes.
We also produce bespoke finishes and furniture within short lead times to ensure you get the tailor made solution for your living space and decor.

Off The Wall , 2 Heyford Court, Hillam Road Industrial Estate, Canal Road, Bradford, BD2 1QJ
Telephone: +44 (0) 1274 302830 Fax: +44 (0) 1274 302831 sales@off-the-wall.tv www.off-the-wall.tv

Courses and Qualifications:
Your guide to getting qualified

The industry this year has flourished with new opportunities presented by the expansion of options for design enthusiasts to become fully qualified professional designers. For some time now, industry bodies have been promoting the importance of working as a professional in a reflected environment and now it seems the faculties and schools are taking note and launching courses of varied length and qualification that cater to the wider design community. Whether it is a BA Hons degree in interior design that needs to be achieved within a one year timeframe or a lengthy university application to becoming a qualified interior architect, the industry as a whole is recognising the need to provide potential designers with the tools to succeed. As a professional designer, having knowledge of the types of courses available is always an advantage when it comes to expanding within your design practices. As a novice designer, there has never been a better time to become a professional in the field you're passionate about.

Above: KLC School of Design now runs a BA Hons course

AMERICAN INTERCONTINENTAL UNIVERSITY – LONDON

Courses:
Four years Full Time Hons BA Interior Design

Associate of Arts in Interior Design (AA)

Bachelor of Fine Arts in Interior Design (BFA)

110 Marylebone High Street, London W1U 4RY

020 7467 5640
admissions@aiulondon.ac.uk
www.aiulondon.ac.uk

BIRMINGHAM INSTITUTE OF ART AND DESIGN

Courses:
Three years Full Time Hons BA Interior Design Certificate Interior Design

Costa Green, University of Central England, Birmingham B4 7DX

0121 331 5000
enquiries@students.uce.ac.uk
www.biad.uce.ac.uk

CHELSEA COLLEGE OF ART AND DESIGN

Courses:
Foundation Degree (FdA) Interior Design - two years

BA Honours Interior and Spatial Design - three years

Graduate Diploma in Interior Design - one year

Foundation in design and technical drawing skills

16 John Islip Street, London SW1P 4JU

020 7514 7751
enquiries@chelsea.arts.ac.uk
shortcourses@chelsea.ac.uk
www.chelsea.arts.ac.uk

EDINBURGH COLLEGE OF ART

Courses:
BA(Hons) Design & Applied Arts (Interior Design)

Lauriston Place, Edinburgh EH3 9DF

0131 221 6000
registry@eca.ac.uk
www.eca.ac.uk

INCHBALD SCHOOL OF DESIGN

Courses:
10 week Full Time Certificate Interior Design

One year Full Time Diploma Architectural Interior Design

Two years Full Time MA Architectural Interior Design

One year Full Time Post Graduate Diploma Architectural Interior Design

10 Week Interior Decoration Certificate

Interior Design and Decoration Week

Three Week Interior Design Drawing

One Day a Week Part Time Interior Decoration Certificate

Interior Decoration on Saturdays

Online Diploma in Interior Design

7 Eaton Gate London SW1W 9BA

020 7730 5508
interiors@inchbald.co.uk
www.inchbald.co.uk

IVY HOUSE DESIGN SCHOOL

Courses:
Four week Full Time Diploma short courses in: Drawing skills, business skills, and design and decoration for interior design.

One Walcot Gate, Bath BA1 5UG

01225 421 657
ivyhousedesign@tiscali.co.uk
www.ivyhousedesignschool.com

KLC SCHOOL OF DESIGN

Courses:
One year Level 6 BA (Hons) Interior Design

Level 5 KLC Diploma in Interior Design

One year Full Time Professional Diploma Interior Design & Decoration

Blended Learning Professional Diploma in Interior Design and Decoration

10 Week Certificate in Interior Decoration, Part-Time Certificate in Interior Decoration Short Courses 1 Day, 2 Day, 3 Day, 1 Week and CAD

Open Learning Diploma in Interior Design and Decoration

Open Learning Design Your Own Home

Open Learning Diploma in Garden Design

Open Learning Designing with Plants

Unit 503, 5th Floor, The Chambers, Chelsea Harbour London SW10 0XF

020 7376 3377
info@klc.co.uk
www.klc.co.uk

LONDON METROPOLITAN UNIVERSITY

Courses:
Two years Full Time HND
Interior Design

Three years Full Time Hons BA
Interior Architecture & Design

Three years Full Time Hons BA
Interior Design & Technology

**41 Commercial Road,
London E1 1LA**

020 7133 4200
admissions@londonmet.ac.uk
www.londonmet.ac.uk

RHODEC INTERNATIONAL

Courses:
Two year Interior Design
Diploma. Dip H/E 2 year
BA(Hons) & BFA - American
Intercontinental University

**35 East Street,
Brighton BN1 1HL**

01273 327 476
contact@rhodec.edu
www.rhodec.edu

ST HELENS COLLEGE

Courses:
HND in Design for Interiors.

**Brook Street
St Helens, Merseyside
WA10 1PZ**

01744 733 766
enquire@sthelens.ac.uk
www.sthelens.ac.uk

THE GLASGOW SCHOOL OF ART

Courses:
Four years Full Time Hons BA
Interior Design

**167 Renfrew Street,
Glasgow G3 6RQ**

0141 353 4512
info@gsa.ac.uk
www.gsa.ac.uk

THE INTERIOR DESIGN SCHOOL

Courses:
One year Full time diploma
One year Part-time Evening
Certificate

Two year Part-time Advanced
Certificate

Five week Summer Certificate
Ten week Summer Advanced
Certificate

Saturday Introduction days

**22 Lonsdale Road
Queens Park
London NW6 6RD**

020 7372 2811
ideas@idschool.co.uk
www.theinteriordesignschool.co.uk

THE LONDON INSTITUTE - LONDON COLLEGE OF PRINTING

Courses:
Foundation Degree in Interior
Design, Two Years, Full-time.

**Elephant & Castle
London SE1 6SB**

020 7514 6781
j.james@lcp.linst.ac.uk
www.linst.ac.uk

THE MANCHESTER METROPOLITAN UNIVERSITY

Courses:
Three years Full Time Hons BA
Interior Design

**All Saints Buildings,
All Saints,
Manchester M15 6BH**

0161 247 2000
enquiries@mmu.ac.uk
www.mmu.ac.uk

UNIVERSITY COLLEGE FOR THE CREATIVE ARTS AT CANTERBURY

Courses:
Three years Full Time Hons BA
Interior Design

Three years Full Time Hons BA
Interior Architecture

**New Dover Road,
Canterbury CT1 3AN**

01634 888 773
info@ucreative.ac.uk
www.ucreative.ac.uk

UNIVERSITY COLLEGE FOR THE CREATIVE ARTS AT FARNHAM

Courses:
Three years Full Time Hons BA
Interior Architecture & Design

**Falkner Road, Farnham,
Surrey GU9 7DS**

01252 722441
info@ucreative.ac.uk
www.ucreative.ac.uk/interiorsfarnham

UNIVERSITY OF CENTRAL ENGLAND IN BIRMINGHAM

Courses:
Three years Full Time Hons BA
Interior Design

**Perry Barr Franchise St.
Birmingham B42 2SU**

0121 331 5595
info@ucechoices.com
www.uce.ac.uk

UNIVERSITY OF THE ARTS LONDON

Courses:
Three years Full Time Hons BA
Interior & Spatial Design

**65 Davies Street,
London W1K 5DA**

020 7514 6000 x6197
info@arts.ac.uk
www.arts.ac.uk

Events: 2013

Trade shows and exhibitions

Trade shows and design events exist to make the designers job that bit easier when looking for inspiration or searching for new suppliers but they can also be valuable events for you when looking for that special something to complete the design of a room. The majority of shows across the UK will be specially allocated 'consumer days' where they open their doors and let you wonder around the aisles of design ingenuity and speak to the professionals at hand. Some will be interior designers, some fabric makers, lighting experts and trend advisors. You never know what you might find in the carnival that is the design show circuit and the UK has some of the best shows on offer.

THE INTERIORS EVENT   20 – 23 January
NEC, Birmingham
www.interiorsbirmingham.com

A one-stop-shop for new design products and suppliers, the Interiors Event starts the year off with a bang. As one of the largest annual events, the event showcases furniture, lighting, accessories, soft furnishings, flooring, fabric and much more in a simply categorised floor plan, designed to give visitors the opportunity to see as much as possible. Designer highlights include a seminar with Nina Campbell.

....

IDEAL HOME SHOW   15 March – 1 April
Earls Court, London
www.idealhomeshow.co.uk

Whether you have a substantial home project or want to add those finishing touches that make a house a home, the Ideal Home Show has everything you need. With seven dedicated show areas catering to every need and taste. From ideal interiors, to ideal home improvements, with ideal gardens, and ideal gadgets, plus ideal food and housewares, ideal shopping and ideal woman the enhanced sections give you more choice and bigger brands, all under one roof. Plus see exclusive show offers, new product launches and items you won't find on the high street.

....

HOMEBUILDING AND RENOVATING SHOW   2013
www.homebuildingshow.co.uk

NATIONAL SHOW
21 – 24 March
NEC, Birmingham

SCOTTISH SHOW
18 – 19 May
SECC Scotland

SOUTHERN SHOW
29 – 30 June
Sandown Park Surrey

NORTHERN SHOW
1 – 3 November
HIC Harrogate

SOUTH WEST SHOW
16 – 17 November
Bath & West, Somerset

The Homebuilding and Renovating Shows have been designed to help you achieve the very best potential out of your home, creating your dream living space. With shows up and down the UK there is an opportunity for everyone to visit at some point in the year. Experts are on hand for consultations as well as seminars and masterclasses to inspire and engage your creative thinking.

....

RHS FLOWER SHOWS   2013
Various location
www.rhs.org.uk

Including BBC Gardener's World Live and the famous RHS Chelsea Flower show in May, these shows take your design ideas outdoors and focus on the all important horticultural and garden design aspects of designing a home. Visit the website to find out about the range of shows the Royal Horticultural Society has on offer and book your tickets now.

Above: *Images show 100% Design 2012 show*

GRAND DESIGNS LIVE
ExCel, London
www.granddesignslive.com

4 – 12 May

Based on the Channel 4 TV series, and presented by design guru Kevin McCloud, the event is a fantastic, interactive showcase of ideas, design and innovation for every room in your home. With over 500 exhibitors, across seven different sections, covering interiors, gardens, home improvement, self-build, renovations, technology and shopping, there really is something for everyone. Whether you are planning to improve, redesign or simply redecorate your home, you'll find everything that you need, all under one roof at Grand Designs Live. Grand Design Live presents two opportunities throughout the year to visit, the first being in May with a follow on in October.

KBB
ExCel, London
www.kbb.co.uk

19 – 21 May

The dedicated kitchen, bedroom and bathroom show alternates between a London and Birmingham location each year. This year it is based in the capital and promises to offer a plethora of information across the broad spectrum of kitchen, bedroom and bathroom innovations.

LONDON DESIGN FESTIVAL
Various London locations
www.londondesignfestival.com

14 – 22 September

The London Design Festival is a fantastic ten-day event that spans multiple hotspots in the capital of London. As well as the shows that are dotted around the capital, the LDF indulges in some hidden treats across the many neighbourhoods of the city, setting up workshops and networking events to surprise and delight the design customer. Fitzrovia Now has a series of events and workshops set up in showrooms and stores to inspire visitors as well as multiple other locations that have come together to join in the festive period. The Festival is both a cultural and a commercial event. The programme ranges from major international exhibitions to trade events, installations to talks and seminars, from product launches to receptions, private views and parties. The majority of events are free of charge - enabling visitors to participate, listen, learn, commission and make purchases.

100% DESIGN
Earls Court, London
www.100percentdesign.co.uk

18 – 21 September

Situated at Earls Court, 100% is a product-centric show that produces some wonderful concepts rom student designers as well as seasoned pros in the industry. The show itself has been compartmentalised and consists of: 100% Interiors, 100% Office, 100% Kitchens and Bathrooms, 100% Eco, Design and Build and the much revered International Pavilions. Conversations between designers and key industry bodies will certainly give some food for thought in the seminar programmes that run across the show.

DECOREX
Kensington Palace, London
www.decorex.com

22 – 25 September

Decorex invites the design community to gather together for a feast of recognised and up and coming design talent. This year Decorex has moved from the Royal Hospital in Chelsea to Kensington Palace in Perks Field. This new location will also spread into the Orangery at Kensington Palace. Decorex opens its doors to consumers for a day where you can take in the breath-taking designs of some of the UK's best design houses as well as seeing International brands present their latest designs.

Established in 1978 the West One Bathrooms group is best known as Europe's most illustrious and innovative supplier of bespoke bathrooms, renowned for sourcing the most unique products for this special area from all over the world.

West One Bathrooms Ltd has extensive showrooms in the UK, six in London, one in Kent and one in Sussex. They have recently opened a showroom in Oxhott, Surrey.

The new luxurious showroom will feature all of West One Bathrooms Ltd key ranges as well as a full range of outdoor Hot Tubs / Home Spas.

The company together with its JC Delepine showroom in Cannes, offers a highly professional sales and design service from all showrooms to suit a worldwide customer base.

Clients include global architects, designers, developers, yacht builders, international royalty and homeowners all assured of quality products with full backup facilities regardless of the size of product, with most orders being fulfilled from comprehensive stock resources.

Please contact their showrooms for further Information where the staff pride themselves on their friendly and expert advice and our always at hand for the customer.

Battersea:	+44 20 7720 9333
Wandsworth:	+44 20 8704 4000
Knightsbridge:	+44 20 7584 7002
Mayfair:	+44 20 7499 1845
Clerkenwell:	+44 20 7324 0780
Selfridges:	+44 800 123 400
Kent:	+44 1892 548 111
Surrey:	+44 1372 841 730
Sussex:	+44 1342 822 422

Alternatively please visit the West One Bathrooms Ltd website of whereby you can view or download their brochure.

www.westonebathrooms .com
sales@westonebathrooms.com

west one bathrooms ltd.

Destined to create the worlds most beautiful bathrooms.
Established since 1978

Above: Walled Garden project by Ham Interiors

Sourcebook

The sourcebook is a one-stop shop for all your interiors needs, created to guide you through a compendium of brands with designs to make your house a beautiful home. From bespoke lighting to kitchen fittings and amazing artwork, there is a whole world of design waiting beyond these pages. Together with advice from the designers featured in the book and in association with the British Institute of Interior Design, the Interior Design Yearbook: Consumer Edition brings you an array of interiors products to help you fully explore the design potential of your home.

Search over 100,000 antiques and
works of art at the tip of your fingers

www.antiques.co.uk

BUY antiques ▪ SELL antiques ▪ LOVE antiques

Antique & Traditional Lighting

FRITZ FRYER ANTIQUE LIGHTING
23 Station Street
Ross-on-Wye
Herefordshire HR9 7AG
Tel: 01989 567416
www.fritzfryer.co.uk

At Fritz Fryer Antique Lighting we specialise in the high quality restoration of antique fittings. We have an extensive range of antique lights and a broad knowledge of lighting history. We work with clients to create sympathetic lighting solutions for period properties and our on-site workshop repair all fittings, by hand, to the highest possible standard.

Antiques

W.SITCH & COMPANY (ANTIQUES) LTD
48 Berwick Street
Oxford Street
London, W1F 8JD
Tel: 020 7437 3776
Fax: 020 7437 5707
E-mail: info@wsitch.co.uk
Web: www.wsitch.co.uk

This company has been specialising in the reproduction and renovation of antique light fittings for over 200 years, and also carries a vast stock of antique fittings for sale, as well as a range of reproductions manufactured using traditional techniques. We run a full repair, rewiring & renovation service for clients' own fittings.

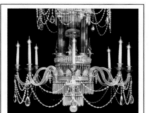

WESTLAND LONDON
Westland London are architectural antique dealers highly renowned for their vast selection of Fireplaces & Accessories, Lighting and antiques of all periods, displayed to great effect in the Grade I listed former church with courtyard in Shoreditch, London, EC2. Our lighting collection includes crystal chandeliers, Gothic brass ceiling lights, decorative French gilt sconces, appliques, torcheres, lanterns and coaching lamps.

View their comprehensive website on:
www.westlandlondon.com
or visit Mon – Fri 9-6, Sat 10-5
St Michael's Church, Leonard Street,
London, EC2A 4QX (Off Great
Eastern street.)
Tube: Old street, Exit 4.
Tel: 020 7739 8094

BUY antiques • SELL antiques • LOVE antiques

www.Antiques.co.uk keeps on growing from strength to strength - the number of buyers locating items they're looking for is increasing exponentially on the site, and with the new seller-notification tools (where any search you save on **Antiques.co.uk** automatically notifies sellers of your wish list so they can add their related items for you to look at), we're turning the antiques world upside down! And don't just take our word for it, the industry gospel, the Antiques Trade Gazette agrees, marking us out for special mention in an article about purchasing antiques online.

Architectural Ironmongery

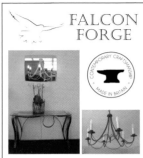

WESTLAND LONDON

Westland London are international architectural antique dealers acknowledged globally for their vast and varied selection of Fireplaces & Accessories, also Lighting including Chandeliers, Paintings & Sculpture, Garden Elements, Fountains & Statuary from all periods displayed to great effect in their central London Grade I listed former church with courtyard in Shoreditch, London.

View their comprehensive website on: www.westlandlondon.com
or visit Mon – Fri 9-6, Sat 10-5
St Michael's Church, Leonard Street, London, EC2A 4QX (Off Great Eastern street.)
Tube: Old street, Exit 4.
Tel: 020 7739 8094.

FALCON FORGE

FALCON FORGE
Unit 3 Omicron House
Fircroft Way,
Edenbridge
Kent TN8 6EL
Tel: 01732 866554
Email: info@falconforge.co.uk
Web: www.falconforge.co.uk

Falcon Forge works closely with its clients providing a metalwork service from concept to delivery, specialising in the design and production of bespoke metal furniture and lighting.
Our trained craftsmen and young design team work with iron, bronze, copper, brass and contemporary steel.

TOUCH IRONMONGERY LTD

TOUCH IRONMONGERY LTD
Tel: 0207 351 2255
Web: www.atouchofbrass.co.uk

Established 30 years ago, Touch Ironmongery is one of London's leading ironmongers. Touch supply a wide range of finishes including Brass, Chrome, Nickel, Copper, Bronze -solid and plated, BMA, Pewter, Ceramic, Leather, Stainless Steel, Gun Metal, and many more. Whatever finish you require, Touch can help you get the right look. Supplying to both residential and commercial developments, Touch Ironmongery reaches all four corners of the world, and their knowledge is unrivalled in the industry. Touch showcases the very best of British manufacturing; still produced in the Midlands by craftsmen in factories dating back 200 years or more. Touch also undertake complete ironmongery refurbishment projects, and can restore old paint covered door furniture to their former glory, looking as new, at a fraction of the cost to replace.

Architectural Features

WESTLAND LONDON

Westland London are architectural antique dealers renowned globally for their vast selection of architectural antiques displayed to great effect in the Grade I listed former church with courtyard, London, EC2. Architectural elements include panelled rooms, windows, doors, antique grilles, gates, fountains & garden ornamentation, columns and plinths.

View their comprehensive website on: www.westlandlondon.com
or visit Mon – Fri 9-6, Sat 10-5
St Michael's Church, Leonard Street, London, EC2A 4QX (Off Great Eastern street.)
Tube: Old street, Exit 4.
Tel: 020 7739 8094.

HAUTE COUTURE HANDLES

HAUTE COUTURE HANDLES BY HARBRINE
Tel: 02089 066548
sales@hautecouturehandles.com
www.hautecouturehandles.com

Design led architectural handles and fittings of the highest quality. Unique styles encompassing hand blown glass, historically influenced designs and unusual material finishes.

TURNSTYLE DESIGNS LTD

TURNSTYLE DESIGNS LTD
Baron Way
Roundswell Business Park
Barnstaple
Devon, EX31 3TB
Tel: 44 (0) 1271 325 325
Fax: 44 (0) 1271 328 248
sales@turnstyledesigns.com

Turnstyle Designs are British designers and manufacturers of some the worlds most unique door, cabinet and bath hardware. Crafting to the very highest quality, a huge range of designs and styles in a diverse range of materials and methods. Suitable for residential or commercial. Bespoke service also available.

Architectural Lighting

DELTALIGHT (UK)
94 Webber Street,
Waterloo,
London, SE1 0QN
Tel: 0870 757 7087
Email: design@deltalight.co.uk
Web: www.deltalight.co.uk

DELTALIGHT® is a global company and we are recognised as being one of the world's largest and most prestigious architectural lighting manufacturers. We offer an extensive lighting collection for interior and exterior use, including an 'eco' and 'bathroom' range. We can also offer you a complimentary lighting design and technical information service, with the capacity to provide lighting calculations and project visualizations.

Art

Mark Firth, 'Instrument', aluminium, wall sculpture, 30.5 x 30.5 x 5 cm, 2011

JILL GEORGE GALLERY
PO Box 657973, London, NW2 9PD
Tel: 0207 439 7319
Email: info@jillgeorgegallery.co.uk
Web: www.jillgeorgegallery.co.uk

The Gallery represents paintings, drawings, monoprints and edition prints by British contemporary artists from the established artist to the recent graduate with sculpture by Mark Firth, Alessandro Gallo and David Mach. The Gallery undertakes commissions and provides all ancillary services from selection to installation. Large selection of work available. By appointment only as Gallery is currently relocating.

Art Deco Murals

Art Frames

INGO FINCKE GALLERY & FRAMERS
24 Battersea Rise, London, SW11 1EE
Tel: 020 7228 7966 (Ben - Framing)
Mob: 07966 276 004 (Kira - Gallery)
E-mail: kira@ingofincke.com
ben@ingofincke.com

Established in 1958, Ingo Fincke is a creative and energetic company providing a variety of framing services, as well as representing established and up and coming artists alike. We offer an extensive range of mouldings, conservation mount boards and speciality glass. Whether it be a small personal job or large contract / exhibition order we are happy to advise you on choosing the right combination for your artwork. We are also delighted to be included in Time Outs essential services directory as one of the best picture framers in London.

LEE FILTERS
Central Way
Walworth Business Park
Andover
Hampshire, SP10 5AN
Tel: +44 (0) 1264 366245
E-mail: sales@leefilters.com
Web: www.leefilters.com

Get creative with fluorescent lighting! With over 250 colours to choose from LEE coloured Fluorescent Sleeves give your more choice than ever for both interior and exterior lighting projects. LEE also offer a range of glass dichroic filters that include less saturated tones suitable for architectural use.

The trend bible....

Advertise in the 2014 edition of the Interior Design Yearbook Call 01733 385300

Arts & Crafts

HENRY SOTHERAN LIMITED
FINE BOOKS AND PRINTS
2 Sackville Street, Piccadilly,
London, W1S 3DP
Tel: +44 (0)20 7439 6151
Fax: +44 (0)207 434 2019
Email: books@sotherans.co.uk
Web: www.sotherans.co.uk

Founded in York in 1761, established
in London in 1815, Henry Sotheran
Limited has a long and distinguished
history. We pride ourselves on the
quality and condition of our books
and prints and we welcome regular
clients and passers-by alike to browse
our stock in a relaxing and convivial
atmosphere.

Bathroom Accessories

THOMAS CRAPPER & CO. LTD
The Stable Yard, Alscot Park,
Stratford-on-Avon,
Warwickshire, CV37 8BL
Tel : 01789 450522
Fax: 01789 450523
Email : wc@thomas-crapper.com
Web: www.thomas-crapper.com

The firm was established in 1861;
nearly 150 years later we produce
exact, hand-made replicas of some of
our classic products of the past. Not
the usual mass-produced, half-hearted
'reproductions', these are the real
thing - but brand new. All products
are produced either from original
drawings or from items in our private
'museum'. Proper, authentic
sanitaryware, made in Great Britain.

West One Bathrooms Ltd
Destined to created the worlds most
beautiful bathrooms

Please visit our website for more
information and showroom location
www.westonebathrooms.com or
email sales@westonebathrooms.com

Tel: 020 7499 1845

Audio Visual Furniture

Audio Visual Furniture Collection

Off The Wall
2 Heyford Court
Hillam Road Industrial Estate
Canal Road
Bradford
BD2 1QJ
Telephone: +44 (0) 1274 302830
Fax: +44 (0) 1274 302831
sales@off-the-wall.tv
www.off-the-wall.tv

Off the Wall design and manufacture a
stunning range of audio visual furniture
that fits beautifully into any interior.
Their inovitive furniture hides all the
clutter of cables and wires and is
available in a large selection of finishes.
Bespoke finishes and furniture can also
be produced within short lead times.

bathrooms by
Ripples

RIPPLES

Ripples the experts in bathroom design
with 17 showrooms nationwide,
offering a unique selection from ultra-
contemporary to relaxed traditional
designs, stylish modular furniture,
cleverly designed furniture to made to
measure bespoke mirrors, shower
doors, showers, wetrooms, brassware,
accessories and clever heating solutions.

Call **0800 107 0700**
or visit **www.ripples.ltd.uk**
to find your nearest showroom.

Bathroom Furniture

THE MOST STYLISH RANGES OF
BRASSWARE, PREMIUM SHOWER
ENCLOSURES & CONTEMPORARY
BATHROOM FURNITURE

01322 422743
contractsales@crosswater.co.uk
www.crosswater.co.uk

P O R T E R

HANDMADE VANITY UNITS

www.portervanities.com

115 Queenstown Road, Battersea SW8 3RH   T +44(0) 2033 55 1817

Bathroom Taps & Brassware

KALLISTA.

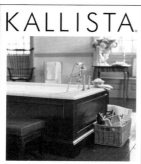

THE BOLD LOOK OF KOHLER AT WEST ONE BATHROOMS LTD.
44-48 Clerkenwell Road
London EC1M 5PS
Tel: +44 2073 240 780
www.KALLISTA.com

Born out of a desire to bring style and a sense of fashion to the bath and powder rooms, KALLISTA® kitchen and bath products combine passion with a profound sense of aesthetic and functional efficiency. Every KALLISTA design is made from the finest materials available, and is created to work in harmony with today's sophisticated interiors.

VOLA STUDIO IN LONDON
32-36 Great Portland Street,
London, W1W 8QX
Tel: 020 7580 7722
VOLA UK LTD
Unit 12, Ampthill Business Park, Station Road, Ampthill, Bedfordshire MK45 2QW
Tel: 01525 84 11 55
www.vola.com

VOLA was designed in 1968 by Danish architect Arne Jacobsen. VOLA continues to introduce new award-winning designs like a new range of free-standing mixers and showers and a new towel warmer concept that received the 2009 GOOD DESIGN Award presented by The Chicago Athenaeum Museum of Architecture and Design and has just been nominated for the German DESIGNPREIS 2011.

Bathrooms

BATHROOMS INTERNATIONAL

BATHROOMS INTERNATIONAL
Tel: 020 7838 7788
Email: sales@bathroomsint.com
Web: www.bathroomsint.com

Bathrooms International is the UK's leading independent luxury bathroom showroom and retailer, selecting, sourcing and supplying exclusive and exotic ranges of baths, sanitaryware, fittings and accessories from around the world. With over thirty years experience and a global reputation, Bathrooms International offers the finest in craftsmanship and the highest quality products for your bathroom.

SAMUEL HEATH
Tel: 020 7352 0249
Web: www.samuel-heath.com

Samuel Heath taps, showers and accessories are crafted from the finest solid brass combining traditional craftsmanship with the latest in design and technology. Design innovation and quality have remained our core values since the company was founded in 1820. Whether for contemporary or classic design; experience a lifetime of appreciation.

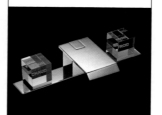

west one bathrooms ltd.

West One Bathrooms Ltd
Destined to created the worlds most beautiful bathrooms

Please visit our website for more information and showroom location www.westonebathrooms.com or email sales@westonebathrooms.com

Tel: 020 8704 4000

HERITAGE®
BATHROOMS

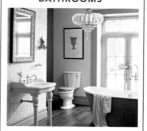

HERITAGE BATHROOMS
Unit 6 Albert Road, Bristol, BS2 0XJ
T: +44 (0) 117 916 8836
marketing@heritagebathrooms.com
www.heritagebathrooms.com

HERITAGE BATHROOMS distributes British designed full bathroom solutions. From sanitaryware, to taps, baths, showers, furniture, heated towel rails and accessories. Whatever your style, whatever your taste, from the classical to the contemporary, Heritage's range of bathroom suites tastefully brings a touch of class to any home.

BAGNODESIGN
LONDON

THG
PARIS

Luxurious Bathroom Fittings

ALBERTO PINTO

Le 11
by Alberto Pinto

Daum

LALIQUE

BERNARDAUD

o.gossart

More info on
www.thg.fr

Like us on
Facebook

Photo THG 2012 © Didier Grier

The **sussex** Range

100% stainless steel towel rails

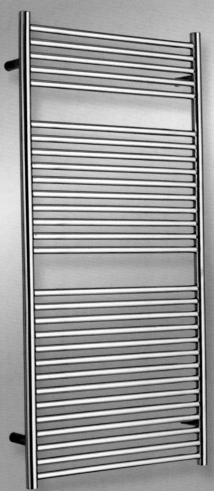

Tel. 01444 831200   Fax: 01444 831900
Email. info@jiseurope.co.uk
www.sussexrange.co.uk

west one bathrooms ltd.

Destined to create the world's most beautiful bathrooms

Battersea	Wandsworth	Knightsbridge	Mayfair	Clerkenwell	Selfridges	Kent	Surrey	Sussex
t 020 7720 9333	t 020 8704 4000	t 020 7584 7002	t 020 7499 1845	t 020 7324 0780	t 0800 123 400	t 01892 548 111	t 01372 841 730	t 01342 822 422

sales@westonebathrooms.com   'At Home Design Service' available see website for details   westonebathrooms.com

It's just a shower, isn't it?

You could say that. Or you could say it's a Samuel Heath 'Fairfield' shower.
You could point out that it's been meticulously formed from the purest
European brass; then hand polished and chrome-plated in up to 34
individual processes. You could say it's manufactured entirely in the UK and
it's passed over 500 hours of salt spray and humidity testing. You could say
it'll last a lifetime. Or, of course, you could insist that it's just a shower.

Discover more about what goes into the most impressive range
of classic and contemporary designs at www.samuel-heath.com
or call 0121 766 4200

SAMUEL HEATH
for a life less ordinary

TAPS • SHOWERS • ACCESSORIES

Bedroom Accessories

Bedrooms

THG - Paris
Tel. +33 322 60 20 80
contact-id@thg.fr
www.thg.fr

Perle was designed thanks to the alliance of three famous names in French decoration: Lalique, Pierre-Yves Rochon and THG. A necklace of pearls engraved on the spout and the cross handles and associated with transparent droplets flowing from the satin crystal. This line brings elegance and modernity to your bathroom.

AND SO TO BED
591-593 Kings Road,
London, SW6 2EH
Tel: 0808 144 4343
Web: www.andsotobed.co.uk

And So To Bed's exclusive beds include traditional and contemporary designs in wood, brass, metal and leather. Bespoke designs, sizes, special finishes and custom upholstery available to order. The collection also includes a wide range of bedroom and occasional furniture as well as luxury mattresses, bedlinens and furnishings to create the complete bedroom.

VI-SPRING LTD
Ernesettle Lane, Plymouth
PL5 2TT, United Kingdom
Tel: 01752 366311
Fax: 01752 355108
Email: info@vispring.co.uk
Web: www.vispring.co.uk

Vi-Spring produced the very first pocket spring mattress more than a century ago. Today every Vi-Spring bed is still handmade to order by skilled Devon craftsmen using only the finest quality sustainable natural fillings, like British fleece wool (including exclusively real Shetland wool), cotton, silk, mohair and cashmere.

Beds & Mattresses

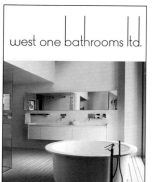

West One Bathrooms Ltd
Destined to created the worlds most beautiful bathrooms

Please visit our website for more information and showroom location www.westonebathrooms.com or email sales@westonebathrooms.com

Tel: 020 7720 9333

A collection of bedcovers, cushions and throws combining clean linear designs with fabulous luxe fabrics. Teamed with fine cotton bedlinens, bespoke headboards, furnishings and occasional upholstery, we have everything you need to create a stylish sleeping environment.

PAD UK Limited
t: 020 7639 3399
e: info@padukltd.com
w: www.padukltd.com

belledorm®

Boasting the most extensive range of plain dyed bedlinen in the UK, belledorm® ensure beautiful sleep for all their customers. Retailers are provided with a versatile and commercial range that guarantees quality along with a personal service which is first class.

belledorm® also offer ranges of designed duvets, comforters, bedspreads, mattress protectors and tablelinen. Their finest Egyptian cotton collection is available in 200 thread count, 400 thread count sateen and 1000 thread count sateen.

The company will respond to any request no matter how large or small and pride themselves on their bespoke service. The design department offer a unique own branding service, providing point of sale with the customers own logo. A friendly service is assured with competitively priced quality products, catering for all markets. With many years of market experience, this company holds a luxury bedlinen brand that is appealing and quality driven.

Their plain dyed collection has no fewer than 30 colours which gives them the accolade of being the market leaders within the UK. Easy care poly/cotton, 100% Egyptian cotton and cotton sateen ensures that all markets are covered.

T: 01204 702 300
F: 01204 793 311
E: belledorm@ruia.co.uk
www.belledorm.co.uk

Hästens

since 1852

We sleep.

Do you?

DAPW
.co.uk

Duvet and Pillow Warehouse
exceptional quality

Luxurious bed & bath products at up to **60% off** high street prices

No fancy shops, no unnecessary overheads. We just work tirelessly to bring you the finest bed and bath products direct from the makers at up to 60% off high street prices.

We guarantee the best prices in the UK, a 365 day returns policy, free standard UK Delivery... and it's all wrapped up in our charming customer service.

Simply the finest quality duvets, pillows, mattresses, bed linen, toppers, towels and much more...

Delivered with happiness

www.dapw.co.uk | 0845 224 5183

Abaca
WILD ABOUT SLEEP

HIDEAWAY BEDS LTD
Unit 1a, Bluewater Estate,
Plympton, Devon, PL7 4JH
Tel: (01752) 511111
Fax: (01752) 511117
info@hideaway.co.uk
www.hideaway.co.uk
facebook.com/hideaway.beds

Many of us have spare rooms not
being used. Why not use it for
practical space such as a home office
or study, whilst still offering
practicality for overnight visitors? A
dual-purpose room is a great way of
increasing your property value and
also its letting potential.

JENSEN SKANDINAVIA LTD
5 Heron Gate, Hankridge Way,
Taunton, Somerset, TA1 2LR
Tel: 01823 444300
Fax: 01823 444340
Web: www.jensenbeds.co.uk

Jensen has been developing high
quality beds and mattresses for over
65 years. Our focus is on consistently
achieving the best possible sleep
comfort in conjunction with excellent
design. We are one of Scandinavia's
leading mattress producers with
distribution in many European
countries. Jensen is part of Hilding
Anders Group.

BIRGIT ISRAEL
251-253 Fulham Road, London SW3 6HY
*Opening Hours: Monday to Friday 10am
to 6pm, Saturday 10am to 5.30pm*
Tel: +44 (0)20 7376 7255
Email: info@birgitisrael.com

Vintage inspired, classic, glamorous
and timeless…Birgit Israel Showroom's
collection 'Made in Germany' is an
expanding line of handmade luxury
furniture and accessories. Produced in
our Hamburg workshop, furniture
items can be made to measure and
feature parchment, piano laquer,
polished brass and wood. Original
vintage and antiques also in store.

Bespoke & Specialist Furniture

HYPNOS LIMITED
Longwick Road,
Princes Risborough,
Buckinghamshire, HP27 9RS
Tel: 01844 348200
Fax: 01844 348099
Web: www.hypnosbeds.com

Hypnos, Royal bed makers and proud
winners of Bed Manufacturer of the
Year 2011/2012, specialise in made-to-
measure handmade mattresses using
the finest natural materials. Personalise
with your preferred divan style, fabric
and feet then crown with a beautiful
headboard to create a unique and
striking piece of bedroom furniture.

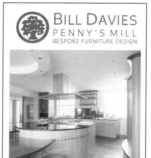

BILL DAVIES PENNY'S MILL
Nunney, Somerset, BA11 4NP
Tel: 07976-606107
Email: billdavies@pennysmill.com
Web: www.pennysmill.com

Bill Davies provides bespoke kitchens and
all kinds of fitted and freestanding
furniture for interior designers, architects,
developers and of course for individual
private clients. Projects range from single
pieces to complete apartments. Styles
and finishes from traditional to cutting-
edge. Curves, exotic veneers and
high-gloss finishes a speciality.

CHRISTOPHER CLARK WORKSHOPS
Sovereign Way,
Trafalgar Industrial Estate,
Downham Market, Norfolk, PE38 9SW
Tel: 01366 389400
Christopher@christopherclark.co.uk
www.christopherclark.co.uk

Specialists in solid timber, painted &
veneered pieces, with established links
to affiliates in glass, metal, stone &
textiles, no detail is impossible for us to
realise. Our flexibility allows us to
initiate designs in house or to interpret
your requirements. With contracts
completed worldwide we have an
international reputation & are very
proud of our continuing work for many
of the top interior designers.

MARK BRAZIER-JONES

Hyde Hall Barn, Buckland,
Buntingford, Herts, SG9 0RU
Tel: 01763 273599
Fax: 01763 273410
Web: www.brazier-jones.com
Email: studio@brazier-jones.com

Mark Brazier-Jones has been creating
furniture and lighting for over 20
years. Working with precious metals
such as bronze and aluminium, and
glass lenses and crystals on his
lighting, Mark's design has influenced
many. As well as bespoke pieces
unique to individual clients
requirements, Mark has a collection
of work that can be made to order.

PAUL LEVY DESIGN
Tel: +44 (0)1622 356634
Mob: +44 (0)7836 220 550
Email: paullevydesign@onetel.com
Web: www.paullevydesign.com

Paul Levy Design offers a design and
manufacturing service for custom
Interior joinery ranging from a single item
of furniture, to an entire room. We also
offer a similar service for bespoke China
Ware and unique Hand Painted Wash
Basins. Our services extend world wide.
Please contact us for more information.

SIR WILLIAM BENTLEY BILLIARDS
Dering Estates, Marten,
Wiltshire, SN8 3SJ
Tel: +44 (0) 1264 731 210
Fax: +44 (0) 1264 731 480
www.billiards.co.uk
sales@billiards.co.uk

Specialists in fine Antique Billiard Tables,
restoration & reproduction. Designers &
makers of contemporary & classic
Snooker & Pool tables, including our
renowned dual-purpose dining tables.
Beautifully handcrafted bespoke tables,
matching accessories & stunning lighting,
made in England from the finest woods &
metals. Worldwide delivery & installation.

Decorus is a reliable, established and valuable
resource for residential and commercial interior
designers and architects. The Company offers
a unique and beautiful collection of furniture,
lighting and decorative accessories in a wide
range of materials and finishes, all of which
can be custom sized or finished.

In addition to our own range of products,
Decorus offers a truly bespoke design and
manufacturing service. We are constantly
working with designers to create one-off
commissions, as well as supplying bespoke
solutions for large commercial projects. From
an initial brief our clients always receive a
considered and viable solution, followed by
professionally presented technical drawings
and comprehensive project management
through to, and including, installation.

To view our collection, and for further information including our latest brochure, please visit our
London showroom on the Kings Road, Chelsea or our website at www.decorusfurniture.co.uk.

Blackbrook

antique and modern furnishings
for every home and garden

Grand & Bespoke Designs at Blackbrook!

Welcome to Blackbrook

an emporium of ANTIQUES, furnishings and furniture **for your home** and WATER FEATURES STATUARY, ANIMALIER, ARCHITECTURAL PIECES **for your garden** and so much more...

Open 7 days a week
Mon – Fri
9.00am – 5.00pm
Sat – Sun
9.30am – 5.00pm

Services we provide

- Team of expert valuers
- In-house interior design experts
- Craft workshops (including the latest in furniture upcycling and chalk painting)
- Bespoke masonry from our team of dedicated masons
- Engraving (stone, glass, wood and metals)
- Garden design and consultancy
- Delicious food and drink in our charming tea rooms

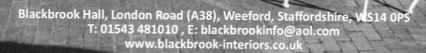

Blackbrook Hall, London Road (A38), Weeford, Staffordshire, WS14 0PS
T: 01543 481010 , E: blackbrookinfo@aol.com
www.blackbrook-interiors.co.uk

Bespoke Carpets & Rugs

Bespoke Leather Furnishings

THE DINING ROOM SHOP
62 White Hart Lane
London SW 130PZ
Tel: 020 8878 1020
Fax: 020 8876 2367
enquiries@thediningroomshop.co.uk
www.thediningroomshop.co.uk

Antique or bespoke furniture in
formal and informal styles for dining
rooms and kitchens is supplied, also
dining accessories, china, cutlery,
glass, lighting and linen.
Tablecloths made to order.
Furniture, china, silver and glass
restoration and interior decorating
services a speciality. Established
1985…well-known destination shop.

AMY KENT
Tel: 07979 594651
Email: info@amykent.co.uk
Web: www.amykent.co.uk

'Amy Kent' is a beautiful collection of
hand knotted rugs, made from a mix
of wool and art silk. They are simple
designs that are both classic and
contemporary, suiting traditional and
modern interiors alike. All the rugs are
made to order and can be individually
customized to any size and colour.

PUGH'S ANTIQUES - Antiques,
Antique Furniture and Replicas
Portley House, North Road
Leominster, HR6 0AA
Tel: +44 (0)1568 616646
Web: www.pughsantiques.com
Email: sales@pughsantiques.com

Pugh's Antiques offers a mix of English
and French antiques, our range
includes chairs, sofas, beds, armoires,
wardrobes and commodes. We have a
range of high quality real leather sofas,
armchairs and furniture with a vintage
effect finish, in traditional, classic and
contemporary styling.

Bespoke Bedroom Furniture

Bespoke Fabrics

Bespoke Wall Finishes

ASHCOLES COLLECTION LTD
Unit 2 Lime Kilns Business Park,
Hammonds Way, Off Nutts Lane,
Hinckley, Leics, LE10 3EJ
Tel: 01455 890582
Fax: 01455 891845
www.ashcolescollection.co.uk

We are master upholsterers to architects,
interior designers, online and high street
retailers. Working closely with our
partners, our collection will sit elegantly
in any roomset. Chairs, sofas, pews,
ottomans, chaises and headboards.
25 years of design and manufacturing.

TRADE EIGHTY
63-65 Riding House Street
London
W1W 7EH
Tel: +44 (0)20 7637 5188
Fax: +44 (0)20 7637 5187
E-mail: trade80@btconnect.com
Web: www.trade80silks.co.uk

Trade Eighty have been inspiring the
interiors industry with their unique
collection of Silks for over 20 years.
Be it plains, shot, metallic silks,
Jacquards, emroideries or Prints, we can
help. Special commissions have always
been offered with nominal or reasonable
minimums and quick delivery schedules
making it all very welcome.

METALL-FX
Unit Oak & Beech
Membury Industrial Estate
Ramsbury Road
Lambourn Woodlands
Hungerford
Berkshire, RG17 7TJ UK
Tel: +44 (0) 1488 726 88
Email: info@metall-fx.com
Web: www.metall-fx.com

Metall-FX are a team of highly skilled
artisans specialising in the application of
real metal finishes to virtually any
substrate. Working closely with interior
designers, architects and artists we
ensure that creativity is never
compromised and that we always provide
all the guidance and expertise required to
deliver truly breathtaking results.

Bespoke Wallpaper

**DAVID OLIVER LTD. T/AS
PAINT & PAPER LIBRARY**
3 Elystan Street, Chelsea,
London, SW3 3NT
T: +44 (0)20 7590 9860
E: info@paintlibrary.co.uk
W: paintlibrary.co.uk

With a beautifully designed paint
palette of 240 chromatically arranged
colours, including 50 that are new for
2013, along with complementary
hand-printed fabrics and wallpapers by
David Oliver and a bespoke Colour
Consultation service, Paint & Paper
Library makes it simple to create
inspiring outcomes every time. Please
email for hand painted colour cards,
brochures, cuttings and stockist details.

Built In Appliances

MIELE
Miele London Gallery
15/19 Cavendish Place
London, W1G 0QE

Miele Experience Centre
Fairacres, Marcham Road
Abingdon, Oxon,
OX14 1TW
Miele.co.uk
T: 0845 365 6610

Miele is a German manufacturer of
high quality domestic appliances and
commercial equipment. Visit Miele's
stunning showrooms at the Experience
Centre in Abingdon, Oxfordshire or the
Miele Gallery, in Central London.
Whatever your plans for your kitchen,
you'll find everything you need to bring
them to life at a Miele Showroom.
Book an appointment, come in and
you'll find inspiration at every step.

Carpets & Rugs

UK SALES: HOME FOUNDATIONS
Tel: 01675 433070
Fax: 01675 430222
sales@heugahomefoundations.co.uk
www.heuga.com
facebook.com/Heugahomeflooring

Heuga offers high quality modular
flooring in a wide range of colors and
textures. Heuga gives you the freedom
to adapt each collection to your own
specific needs with a product that's
easy to choose, install and care for,
with endless possibilities. Go to
www.heuga.com and see for yourself.

custom handmade rug design & consultancy

LOOPHOUSE
88 Southwark Bridge Road,
London SE1 0EX
Tel: 020 7207 7619
Email: info@loophouse.com
Web: www.loophouse.com

Loophouse is a contemporary design
studio based in London, specialising in
custom handmade 100% wool rugs
and carpets. Loophouse was founded in
1992 by Lorraine Statham. With her
experienced in-house team, Statham
has made Loophouse a leading name in
the contemporary rug industry.
Signature design, custom offerings, and
service experience allow Loophouse to
fulfil a client's brief beyond expectations.

MATTHEW WAILES (LONDON) LTD
Unit 0.15 (Ground Floor)
Worlds End Studios,
132-134 Lots Road,
Chelsea, London SW10 0RJ
Tel: 020 7349 7168
Email: info@matthewwailes.com
Web: www.matthewwailes.com

With over 25 years experience,
Matthew Wailes specializes in the
design, production and installation of
the finest hand and machine made
bespoke carpets and rugs for both
residential and commercial applications.
We have also recently added a
luxurious collection of exclusive Hand
Loomed Cashmere Throws/Bedspreads.

Parsua

Editeur de la decoration, Parsua
tailors each creation to suit the
interior. Blending classic styles
with contemporary creations,
Parsua marries East and West
in an original and innovative
way to create objects of ethical
luxury.

LONDON Showroom
C. John - 70, South Audley Street
Mayfair, W1k 2RA
Tel.: +44 20 7493 5288
cjohn@dircon.co.uk

UK Agent
John Miners
Tel.: +44 1787 477875
Mob.: +44 7940 510480
john.miners@btinternet.com

Brontë Carpets Ltd

Over the last 30 years Bronte Carpets has grown to become the longest established custom made carpet manufacturers in the UK.

With our flexible manufacturing process we are able to offer a truly bespoke product with carpets available in any width up to 12 metres wide without seams, in any colour and even made to shape to reduce waste, creating carpets that are as individual as your home and providing the very best quality and service.

Our ranges include 100% wool Saxony, Velvet & Shag Piles, 80/20 twist pile and Hand Crafted Borders.

• Any Colour   • Any Width   • Made to Plan

t. 01282 862736 **f.** 01282 868307   **e.** office@brontecarpets.co.uk   www.brontecarpets.co.uk

RAMA CARPETS

SPECIALISTS IN FINE PERSIAN RUGS

RAMA CARPETS
41 Humber Road
Staples Corner
London NW2 6EN
Tel: 0845 521 1010
info@ramacarpets.com
www.ramacarpets.com

As one of the largest wholesalers of
carpets & rugs in the UK, we offer the
widest range of fine Persian wool and
silk carpets individually selected
from Iran.

Ceiling Fans

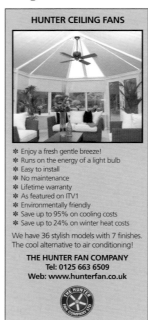

HUNTER CEILING FANS

❋ Enjoy a fresh gentle breeze!
❋ Runs on the energy of a light bulb
❋ Easy to install
❋ No maintenance
❋ Lifetime warranty
❋ As featured on ITV1
❋ Environmentally friendly
❋ Save up to 95% on cooling costs
❋ Save up to 24% on winter heat costs

We have 36 stylish models with 7 finishes.
The cool alternative to air conditioning!

THE HUNTER FAN COMPANY
Tel: 0125 663 6509
Web: www.hunterfan.co.uk

Designers and Manufacturers of bespoke
structures in hardwood and glass.
Contemporary and Traditional Glass
extensions • Skylights and Lanterns
Sliding folding door systems
design • planning • listed buildings
conservation specialists • appeals

BARTHOLOMEW
Rakers Yard, Milland,
West Sussex GU30 7JS
01428 742800
www.bartholomewglass.com
studio@bartholomewglass.com

---

tania johnson design

bespoke, contemporary
hand knotted rugs

info@taniajohnsondesign.com
www.taniajohnsondesign.com

Conservatories

APPEAL HOME SHADING
6 Vale Lane, Bedminster, Bristol, BS3 5SD
Tel: 0800 975 5757
Fax: 0117 378 2019
Email: info@appealshading.com
Web: www.appealshading.com

Appeal offers a range of beautiful blinds
which can instantly transform the look
and temperature of the conservatory.
Appeal Conservatory Blinds are available
in various fabrics and styles and can be
colour matched to whatever shade you
require. Appeal also offers a range of
window shutters for the home.

Contemporary Art

CATHERINE
LOVEGROVE
MURALS

trompe l'oeil

www.clmurals.com
info@clmurals.com
+44 (0)7831 529525

Contemporary Lighting

MARK BRAZIER-JONES

Hyde Hall Barn
Buckland
Buntingford
Herts, SG9 0RU
Tel: 01763 273599
Fax: 01763 273410
Web: www.brazier-jones.com
Email: studio@brazier-jones.com

Mark Brazier-Jones has been creating
furniture and lighting for over 20
years. Working with precious metals
such as bronze and aluminium, and
glass lenses and crystals on his
lighting, Mark's design has influenced
many. As well as bespoke pieces
unique to individual clients
requirements, Mark has a collection
of work that can be made to order.

Coving

DAVUKA GRP LTD
Unit 2c The Wend
Coulsdon
CR5 2AX
Tel: 020 8660 2854
Fax: 020 8645 2556
Email: info@davuka.co.uk
Web: www.davuka.co.uk

Suppliers of fine quality decorative
mouldings, nationwide. Comprehensive
range of interior cornice, skirting, corbels,
columns, dado, architrave, ceiling roses
etc, all as fitted in top international hotels
and developments. See our website for
inspirational ideas and designs or phone
for catalogue and/or samples. Trade
discounts available.

Curtain Poles & Hardware

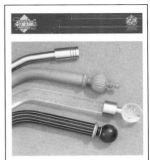

HUNTER & HYLAND LTD
201-205 Kingston Road,
Leatherhead, Surrey, KT22 7PB
Tel: 01372 378511
Fax: 01372 370038
enquiries@hunterandhyland.co.uk
www.hunterandhyland.co.uk

Hunter & Hyland specialise in curtain
poles and tracks which are made to
order. In addition to a vast catalogue
of standard products and finishes our
extensively equipped factory can
produce a solution for almost any
window including angled or curved
bay windows. The choice is limited
only by your imagination.

SILENT GLISS
Tel: 01843 863 571
Email: sales@silentgliss.co.uk
Web: www.silentgliss.co.uk

Silent Gliss offer the Metropole range
of decorative and functioning curtain
poles. This tracked pole requires no
curtain rings since the curtains hang
from gliders contained within the pole
itself. Metropole is available hand or
cord operated in a wide range of pole
colours and sizes. Choose from
traditional and contemporary designed
finials, midials and holdbacks.

Curtains & Blinds

APPEAL HOME SHADING
6 Vale Lane, Bedminster, Bristol, BS3 5SD
Tel: 0800 975 5757
Fax: 0117 378 2019
Email: info@appealshading.com
Web: www.appealshading.com

Appeal offers a range of stylish Window Shutters which can instantly transform the look and atmosphere of any room. Appeal Window Shutters are available in a variety of designs and finishes and can be colour matched to whatever shade you require. Appeal also offers a range of blinds for conservatories.

SILENT GLISS
Tel: 01843 863 571
Email: sales@silengliss.co.uk
Web: www.silentgliss.co.uk

Silent Gliss produces a comprehensive range of window treatment products, including their renowned curtain track and pole systems, in addition to an unparalleled collection of blinds and fabrics to meet every requirement. Over the years Silent Gliss has developed a reputation throughout the world for quality, reliability and innovation coupled with technical perfection and customer service.

Decorative Accessories

HEICO FASTENERS UK LTD
Sirdar Road, Rayleigh, Essex, SS6 7XF
Tel: 01268 745421
Fax: 01268 745467
Email: sales@heico-direct.co.uk
Web: www.heico-direct.co.uk

Our exciting new range of contemporary 'Crystal Nails & Buttons' offers a creative inspiration for your design. The striking beauty of the 'Powder Coated' and traditional elegance of the 'Upholstery' ranges are complemented by our accessories range including Sofa Legs and Brass Castors, providing that innovative touch to your project.

Cushions & Throws

GRANTS BESPOKE BLINDS
T: 0800 652 2190
F: 01983 720949
www.grantsblinds.com

We work closely with Interior Designers, Specifiers and Blinds Specialists Designers to provide reliable shading solutions for both traditional and contemporary interiors. We specialise in conservatories blinds and Wooden Shutters as well as individual specialist requirements for motorized blinds, or blinds integrated to home automation etc. We work nationwide - Designed solutions for managing light & shade.

Luxury faux fur for the home

MOORE AND MOORE
Drayford Lane, Witheridge
Tiverton, Devon EX16 8PR
Tel: 01884 860900
enquires@mooreandmooredesign.com
www.mooreandmooredesign.com

Moore and Moore are the UK's premier designers and makers of luxury faux fur for the home. The range includes throws, bed runners, comforters, cushions and fabulous hot water bottle covers all beautifully handmade in the UK. Using only the most sumptuous fabrics, coupled with a passionate attention to detail, this stunning range will enhance any home.

REDLOH HOUSE FABRICS
Tel: 020 7371 7787
info@irvingandmorrison.com
www.irvingandmorrison.com

Irving & Morrison create beautiful lampshades, ottomans and cushions using one-off fabrics collected from around the world, and have an eclectic selection of lamps and mirrors. In addition to the permanent stock, which you can order on-line or by visiting the London showroom, they also make exclusive items to order.

A shade more interesting...

Wooden shutters create a soft, diffused light for any interior. Choose them in white, bright primary colours or colour matched to your specification - make the colour fit the mood.

Check out our designer colour range of **french pinoleum conservatory blinds** - perfect for country house chic or urban mimialism. We can also colour match to the shade of your choice.

Call us on 0800 652 2190
or email sales@grantsblinds.com

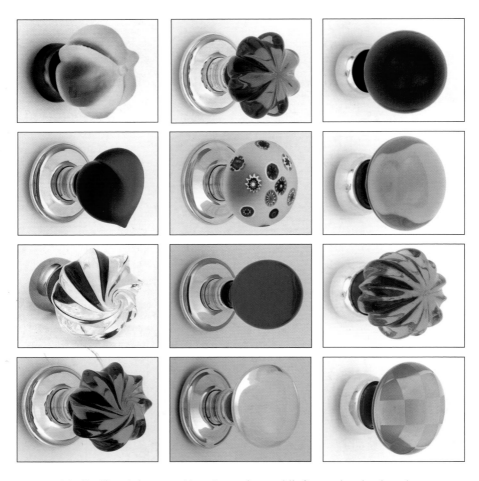

Decorative Glass

Decorative Lighting

KATE FORMAN DESIGNS LTD
Long Barn North, Sutton Manor Farm,
Bishops Sutton, Alresford,
Hants SO24 0AA.
T: +44 (0) 1962 732244
F: +44 (0) 1962 736644
E: info@kateforman.co.uk

Kate Forman Designs specialises in
printed floral linens and wallpapers
inspired by 19th century French
designs. The company also sells a
range of accessories such as cushions,
lampshades and boxfiles.

JO DOWNS HANDMADE GLASS
Unit 27g, Pennygillam Way,
Pennygillam, Launceston,
Cornwall, PL15 7ED
Tel: 01566 779779
Email: sales@jodowns.com
Web: www.jodowns.com

One of the world's most prominent
fused glass artists, British designer Jo
Downs' handcrafted work is inspired
by the coastal setting of her Cornwall
studio. Alongside her much sought
after statement interior objects, Jo has
developed her studio to undertake
large architectural and home interior
projects by private commission.

Decorative Laminates

Decorative Panels

MERLIN GLASS
Tel: +44(0)1579 342399
Web: www.merlinglass.co.uk

Merlin Glass is home to Liam Carey
the world's finest glass knob maker
for doors, kitchens and furniture.

A collection of unique designs in
beautiful colours and finish options,
free design service offered, lifetime
guarantee.

Merlin Glass the ultimate in luxury
glass knobs

FORMICA GROUP
11 Silver Fox Way, Cobalt Business
Park, Newcastle Upon Tyne, NE27 0QJ
Tel: 0191 259 3512
samples.uk@formica.com
www.formica.com

Formica Group globally leads the
industry in the design, manufacture
and distribution of innovative
surfacing products for commercial
and residential applications.
Innovative and complementary
products include High Pressure
Laminate (HPL) in a wide selection of
colours, designs and textures. HPL is
robust, hygienic, and offers countless
design and application opportunities.

filigrana
Tel: 07810 695 627
filigrana.garcia@virgin.net
www.filigrana.co.uk

filigrana design offers a range of
bespoke contemporary pieces
including panels, screens and mirrors
based on the traditional technique
of verre eglomise (gilding on glass),
using soft warm silver tones for depth
of colour, to create visually delicate
eglomise glass pieces.

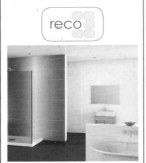
Design Consultants

Designer Furniture

Domestic Kitchens

bulthaup
Holland Park
142 - 144 Holland Park Avenue
London
W11 4UE
T +44 (0)20 7822 2800
F +44 (0)20 7221 7209
www.bulthaup-holland-park.co.uk

bulthaup
Mayfair
37 Wigmore Street
London
W1U 1PP
T +44 (0)20 7495 3663
F +44 (0)20 7495 0139
www.bulthaup-mayfair.co.uk

bulthaup
Clerkenwell
36-42 Clerkenwell Road
London
EC1M 5PS
T +44 (0)20 7317 6000
F +44 (0)20 7490 0840
www.bulthaup-clerkenwell.co.uk

POGGENPOHL UK
100 London Road,
St Albans, Herts AL11 1NX
Tel: 01727 738100
Fax: 01727 738181
info@uk.poggenpohl.com
www.poggenpohl.com

Poggenpohl kitchens are recognised
around the world for their
uncompromising quality and style,
innovative engineering and
pioneering design.
Individually manufactured to order in
Germany, they are available
exclusively from a network of
specialist Poggenpohl Design Studios
across the UK.

**LEADERFLUSH SHAPLAND
ARCHITECTURAL HARDWARE**
Milnhay Road, Langley Mill,
Nottingham, NG16 4AZ
Tel: 01773 530500
Fax: 01773 530040
enquiries@leaderflushshapland.co.uk
www.leaderflushshapland.co.uk

Leaderflush Shapland the UK's leading
performance doorset manufacturer also
offers a range of architectural hardware
to provide a complete end-to-end
solution for a total doorset package.
Each product has been chosen to meet
all technical performance requirements;
a full specification support team is
available with fully trained and
experienced members of the Guild of
Architectural Ironmongers.

Door & Window Ironmongery

ELITE TRADE KITCHENS LTD
90 Willesden Lane
Kilburn
London
NW6 7TA
Office: 020 7328 1234
Fax: 020 7328 1243
Mobile: 07739 077000
www.elitekitchens.co.uks
sales@elitekitchens.co.uk

Since 1985, Elite Trade Kitchens Ltd
have specialized in supplying the
construction, refurbishment and fit-out
sector with high-quality rigid kitchens,
at competitive trade prices. We also
manufacture Office Tea Points/ Break-
out Areas/Post & Copy Points and Light
Commercial Kitchens all of which have
been installed in many Award-Winning
commercial office buildings.

ARCHITECTURAL COMPONENTS LTD
Unit 2, 25 Effie Road, near Fulham
Broadway, London, SW6 1EL
T: 020 7751 3397
F: 020 7736 1282

* London's specialist supplier of high
  quality British & European door, window
  and cabinet hardware as well as
  bathroom accessories.
* Now relocated to our new showroom in
  Fulham.
* Stocks held of all associated locks, latches
  bolts, hooks, hinges & architectural
  ironmongery.
* Stockist of Samuel Heath bathroom
  products
* Order from comprehensive online
  catalogue

www.doorhandles.co.uk

MANITAL SRL
Via delle Quadre, 3
25085 Gavardo (BS) Italy
Tel: +39.0365.3307
Fax: +39.0365.376384
www.manital.com
info@manital.com

MANITAL SRL UK
CARLISLE BRASS LTD, Parkhouse Road,
Kingstown, Carlisle, Cumbria, CA3 0JU UK

CLINIA design Mario Mazzer is a door
and window handle of balanced
proportions with squared lines,
characterized by the grip sloping
downwards. Available in many
finishings: polished brass, satin brass,
satin bronze, chrome, satin chrome,
satin nickel, "SDF" ("Super Durable
Finish", high-performance protective
treatment developed to maintain the
color and gloss in the long run).

bulthaup

New ideas for arranging your kitchen and living spaces. New ways to design your home in exactly the way you want. The latest information about bulthaup. That – and a lot, lot more – is what we, your specialists in new kitchen architecture, can offer you.

Cameron Interiors. 458-462 Crow Road. Glasgow. tel 0141 334 9532
Kitchensplus. 31-35 Marchmont Road. Edinburgh. tel 0131 228 2006
Callum Walker Interiors. Ruthvenfield Road. Perth. tel 01738 638 822

Door Handles

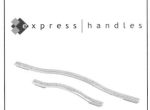

EXPRESS HANDLES
Tel: 01772 218080
Fax: 01772 218081
sales@expresshandles.com
www.expresshandles.com

At Express Handles, we have an
extensive collection of beautifully
crafted kitchen handles and knobs,
ideal for both classical and modern
kitchen designs. Our range
accommodates all preferences from
traditional wooden themes to crystal
and granite, all at great prices.

Contact us today for a full
brochure or consultation
at sales@expresshandles.com.

Eco Products

SALES OFFICE
Tel: 0207 3862694
info@recosurfaces.com
www.recosurfaces.com

Reco is the future of waterproof walling.
These stunning panels can be installed in
a third of the time it would take to tile.
No-grout means no-maintenance.
All panels 100% recyclable. 10 year
guarantee. Designer range / bespoke
images and designs available.

RECO LTD
Enterprise House, Priory Road,
Freiston, Boston, Lincolnshire, PE22 0JZ

Fabrics & Soft Furnishings

ANTIQUE DESIGNS LTD
Ash House, Ash House Lane, Little Leigh
Northwich, Cheshire CW8 4RG
Tel: 01606 892822
Fax: 01606 892844
Web: www.antique-designs.co.uk

Beautiful replicas of antique linens
For the last 20 years Antique Designs
has been producing luxury bedlinen,
bedcovers, tablelinen and accessories in a
wide range of sizes. These are made to
traditional old designs and feature
embroidery, drawn threadwork and
crochet work in 100% cotton or linen.

Door & Window Restoration

**TIMBER WINDOW
RENOVATION SPECIALISTS**
Tel: 0800 0277 454
Email: info@ventrolla.co.uk
Web: www.ventrolla.co.uk

Ventrolla Timber Renovation Specialists
• Timber Sliding Sash and Casement
  Window & Door Renovation
• Performance Upgrading using our
  unique Ventrolla Perimeter Sealing
  System
• Sash Removal System Installation
• Replacement Double-Glazed Sliding
  Sash and Casement Windows
• Secondary Glazing
• Complete New Single and Double-
  Glazed Timber Windows
Call or Click for your FREE, no-obligation
survey and quotation.

Entertainment Technology

CUSTOM AUDIO DESIGNS LTD
5 Ridgeway Office Park, Bedford Road
Petersfield, Hants, GU32 3QF
Tel : +44 (0) 1730 269572
comms@customaudiodesigns.co.uk
www.customaudio.co.uk

Established independent acoustics and
noise control specialists offering an
innovative product range designed in
many shapes, colours, sizes and finishes
to satisfy even the most stylish ears.
Whatever your requirement, from
contemporary to classic, everyday to
eclectic, functional to the down right
funky, let our qualified acousticians help
select the right product for your
commercial, industrial or private project.

SKOPOS
Contract Fabrics

SKOPOS DESIGN LTD
Tel: 01924 465191
Email: sales@skopos.co.uk
Web: www.skoposdesignltd.com

Skopos is an ISO9001 accredited
company and has over 30 year's specialist
experience in the design and
manufacture of innovative, high
performance FR contract fabrics for the
hospitality, cruise and healthcare sectors.
In-house manufacturing ensures full
control over the process from production,
make-up, delivery through to installation.

Fabrics & Textiles

ALTFIELD LTD
2/22 Design Centre Chelsea Harbour
Lots Road, London, SW10 0XE
Tel: 020 7351 5893
Fax: 020 7376 5667
showroom@altfield.com
www.altfield.com

Altfield Represent a number of high
end fabric, wallcovering and leather
companies from around the world,
including Architects paper, Brentano
Fabrics, Brochier, Elizabeth Dow, Glant,
Innovations, Moore & Giles Leather,
Pollack, Thesign, Weitzner and
Westbury Textiles, Altfield also have an
expanding collection of Wallcoverings,
Faux Leather and Fabrics. Featured
above: Couture Collection from Glant.

HENRY NEWBERY LONDON
Original furnishing fabrics & trimmings
7G Regent Studios,
1 Thane Villas,
London, N7 7PH
Tel: 020 7281 5088
Fax: 020 7281 3811
Email: sales@henrynewbery.com
Web: www.henrynewbery.com

For discerning designers & specifiers
seeking originality, refinement &
timeless design, Henry Newbery offers
eco friendly fabrics in natural yarns,
with subtle textures & colours, together
with stock & bespoke trimmings
created in its London workshop. Colour
matching & rapid sampling services
available. By Royal appointment to HM
the Queen since 2000.

Tel: 01684 291037
Web: www.kingdominteriors.co.uk

Kingdom Interiors, an online retailer of
designer fabrics and wallpapers
showcasing the largest online collection
with up to 70,000 products including
the most up to date collections.

Suppliers range from the most
prestigious and established names such
as; Sanderson, Harlequin, Morris & Co,
Designers Guild, Clarke & Clarke,
Prestigious Textiles, Zoffany, and
Osborne & Little, to name a few, to the
more boutique style of up and coming
designers.

Browse all the latest collections from
the comfort of your home or call our
friendly and helpful design team.

Keep in-touch on
www.facebook.com/kingdominteriors
or follow us on Twitter for offers.

parris wakefield
additions

Cushions, lampshades and wallpapers designed and made in Britain.

These patterns merge crisp transparencies with bold graphic kaleidoscopes, feeling both painterly and digital.

A perfect way to add that splash of colour to a room.

www.parriswakefieldadditions.com
sarah@parriswakefield.com
Tweet @SPWadditions
Facebook: Studio Parris Wakefield
01379 783048

WATTS OF WESTMINSTER
3/12 Centre Dome, Chelsea Harbour
Design Centre, London, SW10 0XE
Tel: +44 (0) 20 7376 4486
Web: www.watts1874.co.uk

A company with a truly British heritage and a glorious history of supplying such notable establishments as the Houses of Parliament, Watts has been a leading purveyor of very fine textiles and wallpapers since 1874. Watts's international bespoke service and innovative approach transforms both the classic house and the contemporary interior. We believe the only limit to originality is imagination!

ARTEFACTION STONE & MARBLE
Dockrell Complex
Ballymount Road Upper
Dublin 24, Ireland
Tel: 353 1 4089702 /4089703
Fax: 353 1 4089093
Web: www.artefaction.ie

At Artefaction we offer our clients a bespoke chimneypiece service in naturals stones. From period to modern we are uncompromising in our commitment to the finest quality and design. Period restoration and installation service available

Fibre Optics

As acknowledged specialists in Advanced Fibre Optic Lighting Systems, ABSOLUTE ACTION has an unparalleled record of acclaimed installations and a world-wide reputation for quality, innovation and reliability

ABSOLUTE ACTION
DESIGNERS OF FINE FIBRE OPTIC LIGHTING

www.absolute-action.com | Tel: 01622 351000 | enquiries@absolute-action.com

ENGLISH FIREPLACES
Unit 6 The Brows, Farnham Road,
Liss, Hants, GU33 6JG
Tel: 01730 897600
Fax: 01730 897609
E: info@englishfireplaces.co.uk
W: www.englishfireplaces.co.uk

We make beautiful hand carved fire
surrounds from marble and limestone.
Stock designs range from the
contemporary to authentic period
reproductions. In addition we have a
speedy highly cost effective bespoke
service. We supply throughout the UK
supported by a network of
experienced qualified installers.

For your nearest stockist
of Montpellier's award
winning fireplaces or a copy
of our brochure please call
01452 714 800 or log on to
www.montpellier.co.uk

MONTPELLIER
NATURAL STONE FOR EVERY HOME

REAL FLAME
80 New Kings Road, London SW6 4LT
Tel: 020-7731-5025
Fax: 020-7736-4625
sales@realflame.co.uk
www.realflame.co.uk

Since 1974 when Real Flame
developed the decorative gas fire for
the London market, we have been
installing fireplaces in some of the
most important buildings in the
country and domestic situations.
Mostly we help designers with not
only gas fires, but bio ethanol or
electric fires and wood burning stoves.

**Specialist suppliers of exquisite Fireplaces,
Stoves, Fires & Fireplace Accessories**

capital
fireplaces

For our latest brochures or
to find your nearest stockist visit our website: **www.capitalfireplaces.co.uk**

RealFlame

England's Finest Fires

RealFlame

80 New Kings Road, London, SW6 4LT

www.realflame.co.uk

020 7731 5025

arc freestanding
open convector fire

www.flamewavefires.co.uk 0845 257 5028

we manufacture our open convector fires here in Kent and are able offer a unique made-to-measure service for our built-in and freestanding models as well as stocking a wide range of standard sizes - see our website for more information or call us to discuss

ELEMENT 4

www.element4-fires.com

Legend Fires are proud to be the UK Distributor for the **ELEMENT** 4 range and are currently looking for exclusive dealers for these products.

For further information please contact Susan Calvert.
t 01254 695244 f 01254 695255 e info@legend-fires.com www.legend-fires.com
Unit 404 Glenfield Park Business Centre, Blakewater Road, Blackburn BB1 5QH

smart fire
Fires of the future

We can achieve what you can imagine

Our EcoSmart bio ethanol fires can fit into any environment. Come to our design studio and put us to the test. We have installed fires into pools you can swim right up to. We've even built hidden doors in walls with a fire you can see right through with a fish tank above it! We've suspended fire in mid-air without the use of magic!

Traditional, modern or contemporary. Our fires can go anywhere and all you need to do is tell us what size you want the fire box. We just slide it in place secure it.

Job done. It really couldn't be easier. No flue, no hassle, **no problem**.

Smart Fire, 80 New Kings Road, London, SW6 4LT
020 7384 1677   **www.smartfireuk.com**

ROCKINGHAM FENDER SEATS LTD
15 St. David's Square
Fengate
Peterborough
PE1 5QA.
Telephone: 01733 687375
Fax: 01733 687376
Mobile: 07860 361323
E-mail: info@fenderseats.com
www.rockingham-fenderseats.com

Rockingham Fender Seats make bespoke
fireside surrounds for both period and
contemporary properties. They provide
extra seating around the fireplace taking
up very little valuable space. They are
made in many different designs and
materials, including antiqued or polished
brass, brass, bronze and copper,
burnished or polished steel, woods (oak /
mahogany), or any combination of these.

WESTLAND LONDON

Westland London are architectural
antique dealers renowned globally for
their vast selection of Fireplaces &
Accessories and antiques of all periods
displayed to great effect in the Grade I
listed former church with courtyard in
Shoreditch, London, EC2. They also
supply an impressive accompaniment
of firegrates & baskets, andirons,
fenders, firedogs & chenets, firetools,
firescreens & firebacks.

View their comprehensive website on:
www.westlandlondon.com
or visit Mon – Fri 9-6, Sat 10-5
St Michael's Church, Leonard Street,
London, EC2A 4QX (Off Great
Eastern street.)
Tube: Old street, Exit 4.
Tel: 020 7739 8094.

JAYMART RUBBER & PLASTICS LTD
Woodlands Trading Estate,
Eden Vale Road, Westbury,
Wiltshire, BA13 3QS
Tel: 01373 864926
Fax: 01373 858454
E-mail: sales@jaymart.co.uk
Web: www.jaymart.co.uk

Plaza Safe-T-Decor is an extensive
range of textured slip-resistant heavy
traffic vinyl floorings, IMO tested for
maritime useage, offered in traditional
and modern studded designs and
hi-tech metal chequerplate finishes
which will withstand heavy traffic
areas in public buildings, leisure
facilities and   commercial vehicles.

Flooring

SMART FIRE UK LTD
80 New Kings Road, London, SW6 4LT
Tel: 020 7384 1677
www.smartfireuk.com

Our EcoSmart bio ethanol fires can fit into
any environment. Come to our design
studio and put us to the test. We have
installed fires into pools you can swim
right up to. We've even built hidden
doors in walls with a fire you can see right
through with a fish tank above it! We've
suspended fire in mid-air without the use
of magic! Traditional, modern or
contemporary. Our fires can go anywhere
and all you need to do is tell us what size
you want the fire box. We just slide it in
place secure it. Job done. It really couldn't
be easier. No flue, no hassle, no problem.

FLOORWISE
22 High Street, Kegworth,
Derby, DE74 2DA
T: 01509 673974
F: 01509 674841

Hyper underlays are the perfect
choice for any carpet.
To find out more information on how
to choose the right underlay, please
visit our web site:
www.carpetunderlay.net

ROVERS FLOORING LTD
Unit 33 Jubilee Trade Centre,
Jubilee Road, Letchworth Garden City,
Hertfordshire, SG6 1SP
Tel: +44 (0)1462 486586
Fax: +44 (0)1462 486584
Email: info@roversflooring.co.uk
Website: www.roversflooring.co.uk

Rovers Flooring Ltd is a specialist importer
and distributor of engineered and solid
European oak flooring. A unique service
offered by Rovers Flooring Ltd is the
bespoke finishing and distressing of any
type of oak floor to meet the customers'
requirements. Any colour and any finish,
uniquely hand made to order, here in
Letchworth, England.

ask for
hyper
HIGH PERFORMANCE UNDERLAY

underlay with bags of boing factor!

guaranteed · guaranteed

for the lifespan of all types of carpet

The Hyper brand of underlays are manufactured using recycled post industrial foam, and more importantly they are recyclable after their long use. Each of the seven underlays within the range are designed to work best for specific areas of your home. Whether it's the Super High Density (SHD) hyperTREAD for the hallway and stairs, or the High Density (HD) hyperACTIVE for the lounge and dining rooms – these underlays provide a superior combination of luxury, comfort and durability. Available from quality retailers throughout the UK and Ireland.

For more information visit our web site **www.carpetunderlay.net**, alternatively call **01509 673974** or email **mailbox@floorwise.co.uk**

Hyper underlays tick all the boxes when it comes to performance, recyclability, durability and suitability!

 recyclable   **www.carpetunderlay.net**   floor**wise**

WALKING ON WOOD

490 Kings Road,
London, SW10 0LF
Tel: 0207 352 7311
Fax: 0207 351 7311
www.walkingonwood.com
info@walkingonwood.com

Since 1995, Walking on Wood has provided a wide selection of solid and engineered wood flooring in central london. Our craftsmen have designed and installed custom-made parquet wood flooring and herringbone parquet flooring for interior designers, architects, construction companies and home owners. We specialize in bespoke, hand-made, parquet wood flooring that is tailored to each clients style, requirements and budget.

Constant product sourcing and product innovations, ensures that Walking on Wood provides access to the finest quality hardwood timber from around the world delivering the perfect solution for your natural wood floor. Our parquet floors deliver an infinite range of designs from standard patterns such as herringbone, versailles, basket weave, viscount and chevron patterns floors to completely bespoke patterns.

We supply wood floors across london and beyond as far as continental europe, middle east, asia, russia, australia and usa. Our range of engineered floors come from all types of major wood species such as oak, cherry, walnut and many more hardwood varieties. Walking on Wood fit high quality soundproofing for wooden floors, which comply with the latest uk and european building regulations and floors suited to under-floor heating systems. We supply wood floors across london and beyond as far as continental europe, middle east, asia, russia, australia and usa. Our range of engineered floors come from all types of major wood species such as oak, wenge, walnut and many more hardwood varieties.

Have you always dreamed of having a natural stone floor?

Let us turn your dreams into a reality.

Specialist suppliers of limestone, marble and slate tiles and bespoke stone for architectural and interior design projects.

*Call us **now** for free expert advice and a quotation on*

0845 260 8070

sales@amarestone.com • www.amarestone.com

AMARESTONE
...love stone

make an entrance

With over 40 years of experience and one of the UK's largest range of entrance mats, we can fulfil all your matting needs.

For further information please phone:

01373 864926

www.jaymart.co.uk   email: sales@jaymart.co.uk

Fountains

Furniture

STONE AGE LTD
Unit 3 Parsons Green Depot, Parsons
Green Lane, London SW6 4HH
Tel: 020 7384 9090
Stone Age offers an extensive range of
natural stones at three UK Showrooms –
London's Parsons Green, Bristol and
Hertfordshire. We source over 90
limestones, marbles, granites, basalts,
sandstone and slates from around the
world and have a highly experienced and
friendly sales team to advise you on the
best options for your home.
www.stone-age.co.uk
info@stone-age.co.uk

For more stones for floors or walls,
please visit our sister companies:
www.fulhamstone.co.uk
www.berkhamstedstone.co.uk
www.cliftonstone.co.uk

WESTLAND LONDON
Westland London are antique dealers
renowned globally for their vast
selection of architectural antiques
displayed to great effect in the Grade I
listed former church in Shoreditch,
London, EC2. The exterior courtyard's
garden ornamentation and antique
fountains include old English, French,
Italian marble, stone, ceramic, cast
iron and bronze fountains, birdbaths
and obelisks for modest urban homes
to grand estates.

View their comprehensive website on:
www.westlandlondon.com
or visit Mon – Fri 9-6, Sat 10-5
St Michael's Church, Leonard Street,
London, EC2A 4QX (Off Great
Eastern street.)
Tube: Old street, Exit 4.
Tel: 020 7739 8094

ARTE VENEZIANA SRL
Via Cattaneo, 7
30030 Olmo di Martellago (VE)
ITALY
Tel: +39 041 908920
Fax: +39 041 908992
carla@arteveneziana.com
www.arteveneziana.com

Arte Veneziana produces furniture,
mirrors and lightings in Venetian,
French, Modern and Contemporary
style using its creativity to answer the
personal taste of the client.
It follows its product from drawings to
the final production, and it offers
standard articles as well as custom
items, adapted to each project.

Framing & Framers

SURFACE TILES
London Stores in Battersea & Islington
and West Molesey, Surrey.
Tel: 020 7354 7000 (Islington)
Email: info@surfacetiles.com
Web: www.surfacetiles.com

Surface's innovative showrooms feature
beautifully crafted room-sets with
collections by international designers
including Andrée Putman and Patricia
Urquiola. There are thousands of tiles,
mosaic and stone samples to take home
and product brochures for key ranges.
The friendly, expert team is always on
hand to assist with any questions.

PIERS FEETHAM FRAMING
AND RESTORATION
475 Fulham Rd.
London, SW6 1HL
02073815958
pfeethamframing@hotmail.co.uk
piersfeethamframing.co.uk

With over 30 years experience, we
provide a bespoke picture framing,
conservation and restoration service
based on the highest standards of
craftsmanship and materials. From
period gilding to acrylic cases, we
deliver a service both to the public
and trade, including designers,
galleries,museums and restaurants.

CHARLES BARR FURNITURE LTD
Country works, Sunderland road.
Sandy Bedfordshire, SG19 1RS
Tel: 01767 681444
Fax: 01767 681397
Web: www.charlesbarr.com

Manufactures of one of the largest
ranges of hand made traditional style
furniture available in the UK
comprising, Dining, Occasional, Study,
Conference and Bedroom furniture
available in Mahogany, Cherry, and
Walnut timbers. We also offer a
complete bespoke service providing
initial concept drawings through to full
production in any style and timbers.

GREENGATE FURNITURE LTD

St. George's Works, Coronation Road,
HIGH WYCOMBE, Bucks, HP12 3GG
Tel: 44 (0)1494 755 400
Fax: 44 (0)1494 755 405
Email: sales@greengate.co.uk
Web: www.greengate.co.uk

New for 2013 is the CADOGAN chair –
just one of an extensive range of
traditional and modern introductions for
the interior design market. The chair is
shown in Northcroft Fabric's Jean Bart
Gaufrage velvet. See our website for
details of new pieces as they are
introduced throughout the year.
Our showrooms and fabric library are
open Monday – Friday 10 am to 5 pm.

Image: Spyder Collection by Paul Case
Furniture. Dining table and chairs shown.
Lounge furniture also available to match.

PAUL CASE FURNITURE

Fairfield Farm Business Park, Longsight Road,
Osbaldeston, Nr Blackburn, Lancs BB2 7JA
Tel: 01254 813 113
www.paulcasefurniture.co.uk

PAUL CASE
FURNITURE

Shortlisted for Wood
Awards and Northern
Design Awards 2012.

HOT LOBSTER LTD
Tel: +44 (0)1938 558852
Email: info@hotlobster.co.uk
Web: www.hotlobster.co.uk

Hot Lobster is a British furniture
designer and manufacturer, crafting
high quality bespoke furniture for
private and commercial clients. We
produce furniture which is unique,
inherently beautiful and of
exceptional quality.... furniture to fall
in love with. We have also recently
launched our first range: 'Furniture
Your Friends Will Fancy'.

girsberger
seating

GIRSBERGER GMBH
Invicta House,
108-114 Golden Lane,
London, EC1Y 0TG
Tel: 020 7490 3223
Fax: 020 7490 5665
infouk@girsberger.com
www.girsberger.com

The Girsberger product range includes
different types of chairs such as swivel
chairs, conference chairs, visitor chairs
and armchairs, as well as tables, lounge
furniture and sideboards. The newest
addition to the range is the award-
winning CORPO office chair. Fully
adjustable and with various design
options, this unpretentious and yet
highly sophisticated chair offers the
highest comfort and a row of
ergonomic functions.

JONATHAN CHARLES
Unit 6 C, Shortwood Business Park,
Shortwood Court, Dearne Valley Park
Way, Hoyland South Yorkshire S74
9LH, UK
Tel: 01226 741 811
Fax: 01226 744 905
E: charles@jonathancharles.com
www.jonathancharles.com

World reowned Jonathan Charles Fine
Furniture embraces the past with its
timeless reproductions, masterfully
created and expressing exquisite
details with uncompromising
craftsmanship. To add to its ever
growing catalogue is the transitional
Luxe Collection, a new direction for
traditional furniture.

Luxury Fitted Furniture
Made to fit your space exactly

Declutter and reorganise your home with sleek contemporary or traditional storage solutions

Bedrooms | Studies | Media Cabinets

Furniture Designers

CHRISTOPHER CLARK WORKSHOPS
Sovereign Way,
Trafalgar Industrial Estate,
Downham Market, Norfolk, PE38 9SW
Tel: 01366 389400
Christopher@christopherclark.co.uk
www.christopherclark.co.uk

Highly skilled team of experienced
furniture designers, manufacturers &
finishers offering a complete design to
manufacture service of exceptional
quality bench made furniture. Unique
pieces can include collaboration with
specialists in glass, metal, stone &
textiles. We can handle individual pieces
or production runs for commercial or
residential projects.

PHILIPPE HUREL
122 Fulham Road, London, SW3 6HU
Tel: 0207 373 1133
Fax: 0207 373 1134
www.philippe-hurel.com
phlondon@philippe-hurel.com

Philippe Hurel is successor to a
quintessentially French dynasty and
creator of modern furniture remarkable
in its design, build and finish. Rooted in
France, the family led business benefits
from over 100 years of manufacturing
savoir faire, blending traditional
techniques with no-nonsense design.
Offering a complete bespoke package,
Philippe Hurel and his team work on
projects ranging from private
residences, hotels, yachts and luxury
boutiques, through to one-off pieces.

Games Room Solutions

Leading the way in contemporary
furniture **Stuart Scott** combines quality,
style and a lifelong passion for design.

The collection, also available in
Liberty, successfully projects Stuart's
vision to create beautiful handcrafted
furniture with a strong design edge
that is both practical and above
all comfortable to use.

A bespoke service is also offered.

www.stuartscott.co.uk
t +44 (0) 1225 753592

JAMES MAYOR FURNITURE
Tel: 0121 328 1643
info@jamesmayorfurniture.com
www.jamesmayorfurniture.com

As designers and makers of painted,
bespoke, fitted furniture for the entire
home for more than 40 years, our work
features clean lines and well proportioned
shapes. Each piece is handmade by
craftsmen in our workshop in the UK.
An on-site survey and consultancy service
is available for larger jobs.

WALDERSMITH
32 London Street,
Chertsey, Surrey, KT16 8AB
(Company relocation 2013 - London)
M: 07968 850809 Sales & Enquiries
T: 01932 568414 Showroom
E: enquiries@waldersmith.com
www.waldersmith.com

Waldersmith is an enthusiastic family
led team dedicated to supplying
vintage, contemporary and bespoke
games room solutions. Specialists in the
rare and whimsical with a keen eye on
quality and service, the current
portfolio features: refurbished vinyl
jukeboxes, original Coca-Cola
machines and stylish pool dining tables.

Black
&Key

Luxurious Art Deco inspired furniture,
exquisitely handcrafted in England.

+44 (0) 208 741 8010

www.blackandkey.co.uk

Garden Luxury Furniture

THE HEVENINGHAM COLLECTION

THE HEVENINGHAM COLLECTION
Tel: + 44 (1) 489893481
Email: sales@heveningham.co.uk
www.heveningham.co.uk

THE HEVENINGHAM COLLECTION is the ultimate in stylish, elegant iron furniture perfect for the home, terrace, conservatory or poolside. Designs include, elegant dining sets, chaise longue, armchairs and tables, bar stools, benches, Versailles tubs and swing seats which have proved extremely popular with clients in a wide range of locations throughout the World.

Nero Designs offer interpretive and decoration skills gained from more than fifty years of experience, which enable us to supply a unique and professional glass decoration and installation service to clients all over the world, including our new 'Façade' range of cladding and our expertise in edge–illuminated features.

332-334 Brixton Road, London SW9 7AA
020 7737 8021

sales@nerodesigns.co.uk
www.nerodesigns.co.uk

Hardware Flooring

WALKING ON WOOD

490 Kings Road
London
SW10 0LF
Tel: 0207 352 7311
Fax: 0207 351 7311
www.walkingonwood.com
info@walkingonwood.com

Manhattan
1127 2nd Avenue (corner 59th Street)
New York, NY 10022
Tel: +1 212 832 2500
Fax: +1 212 832 2600

Glass & Glazing

ARLA PLAST AB
Box 33, Västanåvägen
SE-590 30 Borensberg
Sweden
Tel: + 46 141 20 38 00
Fax: + 46 141 414 30
Email: info@arlaplast.se

GRIPHEN™ FROST can be used in a variety of applications such as point of sale, interior design, displays, indoor illuminated signs, showcases applications and exclusive design accessories. The product has better fire performance and more than 5 times the impact strength of standard acrylics , is easy to fabricate/thermoform, and the frosty effect stays prominent after thermoforming. GRIPHEN™ FROST is available in any transparent colour.

Gymnasium Equipment

MOTIVE8 GROUP
3 The Mews, 53 High Street,
Hampton Hill, Middlesex, TW12 1NH
Freephone: 0800 028 0198
Tel: 020 8481 9700
Fax: 020 8979 3914
Email: info@m8group.co.uk

motive8 is the market leader in residential gym and spa design, equipment supply and installation. Since 1998, motive8 has fitted over 120 facilities nationwide, including home gyms, spa facilities, private training studios, corporate facilities and large fully-staffed residential sites. motive8 provides maintenance to gyms and has contracts with over 100 facilities.

Home Furniture

BENCHMARK
Bath Road, Kintbury
West Berkshire, RG17 9SA
Tel: 01488 608020
Fax: 01488 608030
sales@benchmarkfurniture.com
www.benchmarkfurniture.com

Excellence in design, materials and craftsmanship form the foundation of Benchmark, producing contemporary classics in a sustainable way that will last several lifetimes. Our furniture has been developed with leading designers, such as Terence Conran and Russell Pinch, as well as up and coming new names and is handmade in our workshop in Kintbury, West Berkshire.

Insurance

Interior Design Consultants

Interior Design Services

Interior Designers

Kitchen Taps & Brassware

HELEN GREEN
LONDON

www.helengreendesign.com
Tel: 02073523344

A comprehensive design studio synonymous with the creation of beautifully crafted interiors. Their work reflects their extensive experience creating luxurious and livable spaces for a wide range of international clients. In addition to their design services, they have developed three collections of British made bespoke furniture, as well as upholstery fabrics and wallpapers.

KEY INTERIORS

Inspired interiors

for private homes and commercial clients,

executed to a high standard

by skilled craftsmen.

t 05601 267 291

mail@keyinteriors.co.uk

www.keyinteriors.co.uk

KWC (UK) LTD
149 Balham Hill, London, SW12 9DJ
Tel: 020 8675 9335
kwcuk@globalnet.co.uk
www.kwc-uk.com

A Swiss company with a long and proud history of invention and precision engineering, KWC Faucets is at the forefront of design and technological innovation in taps, creating beautiful, highly-functional and reliable fittings that are a must-have for the high spec kitchen. KWC is the top kitchen designer's choice.

Internal Doors

Kitchen Appliances

HELEN TURKINGTON
COLLECTION

HELEN TURKINGTON INTERIORS
4 - 5 The Parade, St. Johns Hill, Clapham, London, SW11 1TG
Tel: 020 7228 9435
Fax: 020 7585 1571
Email: info@helenturkington.co.uk
Web: www.helenturkington.com

Helen Turkington is among one of the most influential and talented designers within Ireland and the UK. Her name stands for a unique blend of sophistication and liveability. Helen's homes are as comfortable as they are beautiful, as simple as they are refined and as peaceful as they are powerful. The Helen Turkington collection comprises of furniture, fabrics for curtaining and upholstery, her own paint range and a range of home accessories.

JBKind
DOORS

JB KIND DOORS
Tel: 01283 554197
Web: www.jbkind.com

Inspirational doors – undeniable value. JB Kind offer innovative door solutions with a wide choice of designs to suit contemporary and traditional design themes. FD30 fire doors are available for virtually every door range. Bespoke designs and special sizes can be ordered at reasonable prices. Request a copy of the 2013 brochure.

CDA

CDA
Harby Road, Langar, Nottingham, NG13 9HY
Tel: 01949 862 010
Fax: 01949 862 001
Web: www.cda.eu

CDA is one of the fastest growing appliance brands in the UK, manufacturing a range of over 450 stylish kitchen appliances, sinks and taps including the unique and innovative integrated draught beer dispenser. Uncompromising quality, style and innovation are what make CDA products so special, backed by a 5 year guarantee and industry-leading CDA service engineers.

Lifts

LA CORNUE
14 rue du bois du pont
ZI les Béthunes
95310 Saint Ouen l'Aumône
France
Email: a.table@la-cornue.com
Web: www.lacornue.com

We developed the Cornue W. line in collaboration with the French architect-designer Jean-Michel Wilmotte. This innovative approach to French lifestyle is truly a point of convergence between tradition and modernity. The signature of Jean-Michel Wilmotte makes a true reference for lovers of architecture and design. Models shown: Induction table and hood

RIEBER LIMITED
Unit 6, Lancaster Park Ind. Estate,
Melksham, Wiltshire, SN12 6TT
Tel: 01225 704470
Fax: 01225 705927
Contact: Sally Buchanan
Email: sales@bglrieber.co.uk
Web: www.bglrieber.co.uk

Rieber sink options include highly practical minimalist designs to exclusive models such as the Waterstation Round and Waterstation cubic (which features a 3-tier food preparation area). Waterstation® Round, diameter 902 mm, can be set at different heights ranging from 920 to 1000 mm for any installation situation.

STANNAH
Tel: 0800 715487
marketinguk@stannah.co.uk
www.stannahhomelifts.co.uk

Stannah is an independent leader in lifts, manufacturing stairlifts and selling passenger lifts, escalators, vertical platform lifts and service lifts. Established in the 1860s, Stannah remains a proudly British owned family business. It recently launched a sleek home 'lifestyle' mini-lift, called the Salise, which is aimed at everyday consumers and doesn't require any major structural work to install.

Kitchens

Lighting Control

Experience the world between on and off.

THE BOLD LOOK OF KOHLER AT WEST ONE BATHROOMS LTD.
44-48 Clerkenwell Road
London EC1M 5PS
Tel: +44 2073 240 780
www.KALLISTA.com

Born out of a desire to bring style and a sense of fashion to the bath and powder rooms, KALLISTA® kitchen and bath products combine passion with a profound sense of aesthetic and functional efficiency. Every KALLISTA design is made from the finest materials available, and is created to work in harmony with today's sophisticated interiors.

LA CORNUE
14 rue du bois du pont
ZI les Béthunes
95310 Saint Ouen l'Aumône
France
Email: a.table@la-cornue.com
Web: www.lacornue.com

Today you can celebrate the art of living "à la française" with the Domaines Culinaires. We can design, create and install complete bespoke kitchens with a level of excellence that is unique to La Cornue. With Domaines Culinaires, La Cornue elevates your kitchen to a new level of luxury.

With dimming, switching and shading solutions from Lutron, you can manage the light that surrounds you effortlessly and efficiently. Instantly, your world becomes a more relaxed, secure and elegant space.

Lutron EA Ltd.
6 Sovereign Close,
London E1W 3JF, UK
Phone: +44 (0) 20 7702 0657
lutronlondon@lutron.com
www.lutron.com/europe

Lighting

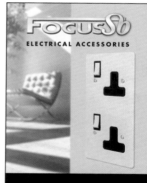

J H Miller

Decorative Lighting Specialists

Exclusive Italian
Lighting to the Trade
sales@jhmiller.co.uk
www.jhmiller.co.uk
Tel: 0161 775 0005

Design your electrical accessories

Our bespoke design and manufacturing service allows you to specify electrical accessories to suit the look and layout of your interiors and the needs of your clients. From initial design and manufacture of prototypes, to short run or mass production, we can help. Call us today for further details.

See how our plates will look in your interior. Download our free RoomView app from the App Store or Google Play.

Available on the App Store

No long lead times | No minimum order | Complete bespoke service

Tel: 01424 858060 www.focus-sb.co.uk

Focus SB
ELECTRICAL ACCESSORIES

Chutney Mary Restaurant, London, UK

Absolute Action have specialised in advanced fibre optic lighting systems since 1983.

With an unparalled record of acclaimed installations, the company has a world-wide reputation for quality, reliability and durability

ABSOLUTE ACTION
DESIGNERS OF FINE FIBRE OPTIC LIGHTING

www.absolute-action.com | Tel: 01622 351000 | enquiries@absolute-action.com

WWW.MAROESKA.COM

MAROESKA.COM
Noorddijk 90
1521 PD Wormerveer
The Netherlands
Mob: 0031.655848100
Tel: 0031.75.6407275
Fax: 0031.75.6407276
info@maroeska.com
www.maroeska.com

Maroeska designs and creates her own Brand since 1988. We have our collection, but we are also producing custom made lighting for every setting. Maroeska's designs will easily fit in both classic or modern interiors.

Paolo Moschino
FOR
NH
NICHOLAS HASLAM

NICHOLAS HASLAM LTD
12-14 Holbein Place
London, SW1W 8NL
Tel: +44 (0)207 730 8623
Web: www.nicholashaslam.com

For nearly twenty years Paolo Moschino has owned and run Nicholas Haslam Ltd. The company comprises of two showrooms in Belgravia and an interior design service. The showrooms stock an extensive range of lighting, furniture, fabrics and antiques with a warm and classic European sensibility. Similarly, Paolo's interior design portfolio boasts an array of projects, which have graced the front cover of many an international magazine.

PRANDINA

PRANDINA SRL
Via Rambolina 29
360361 Bassano del Grappa (VI)
www.prandina.co.uk
www.facebook.com/prandina

Prandina is one of the best Italian lighting manufacturer with an old tradition in blown glass products. Founded in 1982, the company is exporting more than 80% of the turnover in more than 50 countries. Special department for contract projects.

Mirrors

R&D (*demista*) LTD
(A DIVISION OF R&D MARKETING LTD)
Land House, Anyards Road
Cobham, Surrey, KT11 2LW
Tel: 01932 866600
Email: rd@demista.co.uk
Web: www.demista.co.uk

demista was introduced to the market some 20 years ago since when it has been supplied world wide to many market sectors. With its faultless track record it is, not surprisingly, the automatic choice of architects, house builders, hotels, etc. *demista* is internationally approved and carries a 10 year warranty.

KATHARINE KNIGHT MIRRORS

For further information and a brochure please contact:
Tel: 01233 502033
Email: info@katharineknight.co.uk
Web: www.katharineknight.co.uk

Beautiful Mirrors hand made in the UK

Office Furniture

girsberger
seating

GIRSBERGER GMBH
Invicta House,
108-114 Golden Lane,
London, EC1Y 0TG
Tel: 020 7490 3223
Fax: 020 7490 5665
infouk@girsberger.com
www.girsberger.com

Jack is an elegant line of chairs suitable for the most diverse uses – at the conference table, at your desk, or as an easy chair in the lounge. All the versions offer surprising comfort thanks to the seat shell featuring the latest foam rubber padding.

Modern Furniture

filigrana
Tel: 07810 695 627
filigrana.garcia@virgin.net
www.filigrana.co.uk

filigrana design offers a range of bespoke contemporary pieces including panels, screens and mirrors based on the traditional technique of verre eglomise (gilding on glass), using soft warm silver tones for depth of colour, to create visually delicate eglomise glass pieces.

CHAPLINS
LUXURY LIFESTYLE LIVING

THE LARGEST INDEPENDENT MODERN FURNITURE SHOWROOM IN EUROPE

T 020 8421 1779 sales@chaplins.co.uk
www.chaplins.co.uk

PAOLA LENTI

PAOLA LENTI SRL
via Po, 100/a
20821 Meda (MB – ITALY)
Tel: + 39-0362-344587
Fax: + 39-0362-71204
Email: info@paolalenti.it
Web: www.paolalenti.com

Paola Lenti pieces offer a design where colours and dimensions are studied to create harmony without excess; a style which is able to convey an empathy between nature and product. A naturally evolving design that combines architectural structures, seating and rugs, emphasizing the innate potential of each material, colours and shapes.

CHAPLINS
LUXURY LIFESTYLE LIVING

SERVICES
HOME DESIGN SERVICE
INTERIOR ARCHITECTURE
CONTRACT INTERIORS
ART CONSULTANCY
ONLINE STORE

DEPARTMENTS
LIVING
DINING
WORKING
SLEEPING
LIGHTING
ACCESSORIES
OUTDOOR
GALLERY

EXPERTS IN
MULTI-BRAND PURCHASING
WAREHOUSING
CONSOLIDATING
INSTALLATION
WORLDWIDE SHIPPING
OVERSEAS PROJECTS

DOWNLOAD
THE CHAPLINS APP

UK SHOWROOMS

Uxbridge Road Pinner Hatch End Middlesex HA5 4JS | +44(0)20 8421 1779
Design Centre Chelsea Harbour London SW10 0XE | +44(0)20 7352 6195
www.chaplins.co.uk

TURRI®

MADE IN ITALY

22060 Carugo CO Italy Ph +39.031.760111 Fax +39.031.762349 info@turri.it - www.

Bourlet
The Collectors Fine Art Frame Maker

Sculptural work by Nicola Hicks
False rabbit fur frame by Bourlet

Bourlet began making frames almost 200 years ago.

The frames we make today still employ the same skills, materials and techniques.

These skills include gilding, carving, composition, veneers, French polishes and paint finishes.
Our clients include contemporary West End galleries, nationwide museums, contemporary artists and
private collectors. We are equally at home making a box frame or a carved gilded mirror frame.

32 Connaught Street London W2 2AF - Tel: 020 7724 4837 - www.bourlet.co.uk

Paint & Coatings

**DAVID OLIVER LTD. T/AS
PAINT & PAPER LIBRARY**
3 Elystan Street, Chelsea,
London, SW3 3NT
T: +44 (0)20 7590 9860
E: info@paintlibrary.co.uk
W: paintlibrary.co.uk

With a beautifully designed paint
palette of 240 chromatically arranged
colours, including 50 that are new for
2013, along with complementary
hand-printed fabrics and wallpapers by
David Oliver and a bespoke Colour
Consultation service, Paint & Paper
Library makes it simple to create
inspiring outcomes every time. Please
email for hand painted colour cards,
brochures, cuttings and stockist details.

EARTHBORN
Tel: 01928 734 171
Fax: 01928 731 732
www.earthbornpaints.co.uk
facebook.com/earthbornpaints

Launched in 2001 and licensed to
carry the EU Ecolabel, Earthborn paint
has a trusted reputation for
performance and style. Hardwearing,
breathable and with no nasty smells
or emissions Earthborn paints cover
like a dream. To find your local
stockist please visit our website.

Painted Furniture

LEPORELLO
4 - 5 Old Char Wharf, Station Rd,
Dorking, Surrey RH4 1EF
T 01483 284109 Sales & Enquiries
T 01306 875550 Showroom
E info@leporello.co.uk
www.leporello.co.uk

Leporello, specialist designers and
manufacturers of an exceptional range of
painted dining & bedroom furniture and
accessories in both classic and
contemporary styles. Designed and made
in house by master craftsmen. Variable
size options, paint colours & treatments.
Design/bespoke service. Home delivery &
installation + overseas shipping service.

Paving

**With the largest range of colour and
design possibilities available, resin
bound permeable paving from SureSet
make the possibilities endless.**
Fully permeable allowing water to just drain through
and laid onto any flat surface. SureSet will add an
eco-friendly and visually stunning addition to your
outside areas. All of our products are backed by our
15-Year Guarantee and are fully supplied and laid
by our expert team. You will also be fully supported
throughout the whole process.

Contact us for a Free Quotation and Sample:

www.sureset.co.uk

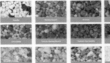

To view our full ranges, please visit our website
SURESET UK LTD
32 Deverill Road Trading Estate
Sutton Veny, Warminster
Wiltshire BA12 7BZ
T: 01985 841180
F: 01985 841260
sales@sureset.co.uk
SureSet
Permeable Paving

Picture Framers

BOURLET

32 Connaught Street
London
W2 2AF
Tel/Fax: 020 7724 4837
Email: enquiries@bourlet.co.uk

Bourlet began making frames almost
200 years ago. The frames we make
today still employ the same skills,
techniques and materials of the old
master frame makers. Our clients
range from contemporary west end
dealers and artists to old master
dealers and national museums and
galleries. We carve, gild, veneer, stain
and French polish.

Plasterwork & Mouldings

DAVUKA GRP LTD
Unit 2c The Wend
Coulsdon
CR5 2AX
Tel: 020 8660 2854
Fax: 020 8645 2556
Email: info@davuka.co.uk
Web: www.davuka.co.uk

Suppliers of fine quality decorative
mouldings, nationwide. Comprehensive
range of interior cornice, skirting, corbels,
columns, dado, architrave, ceiling roses
etc, all as fitted in top international hotels
and developments. See our website for
inspirational ideas and designs or phone
for catalogue and/or samples. Trade
discounts available.

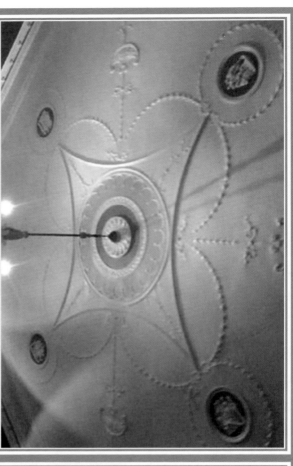

Property Consultants

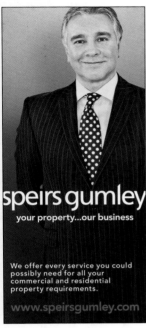

QUINN RADIATORS
Imperial Park, Newport, Gwent, NP10 8FS
Tel: +44 1633 657271
Fax: +44 1633 657151
Email: info@QUINN-radiators.com
Web: www.QUINN-radiators.com

Quinn Radiators is one of Europe's
leading manufacturers of panel &
design radiators. With state of the art
panel & design manufacturing plants in
Newport, Gwent, Quinn ensure world
class standards of high-quality, British-
made products all backed by a 10-year
warranty. With Quinn Radiators you
will always get the radiators you need -
when you need them.

VOGUE (UK) LTD
Tel: 01902 387000
Email info@vogueuk.co.uk
Web: www.vogueuk.co.uk

Vogue (UK) Ltd is one of the only few
remaining British towel warmer
brands to manufacture its own
designs. Producing a comprehensive
range of hand-crafted towel warmers
and designer radiators, Vogue (UK)
Ltd offers a wealth of choice in both
contemporary and traditional styles.

Radiators

Aeon epitomises stylish, sculptural
heating for contemporary homes
available from a nationwide
network of accredited retailers.
Made from high-quality stainless
steel, Aeon designer radiators look
fabulous and deliver exceptional
performance.

The 78-strong collection
(including the Maze above) is
engineered to exacting standards
and each hand-finished product
carries a 20-year guarantee.

Tel: 01908 271155
Email: info@pitacs.com
Web: www.aeon.uk.com

THE GLASS RADIATOR CO.
Tel: 01380 738840
info@glassradiators.co.uk
www.glassradiators.co.uk

Thermovit SGG
Clear glass, stylish & simple, flexible &
energy efficient.
It's exceptionally clear glass ensures total
transparency and clarity. They can be wall or
floor mounted with high quality Stainless
Steel or Chrome fittings, and the extra
towel rail accessory turns this stunning
radiator into a heated towel rail.
The wireless thermostat controlled version
regulates the room temperature, ensuring
maximum comfort and efficiency.
We also do The RadArt Radiator, this allows
any image of your choice on the radiator.
Another product, GRC Treese®
Hand crafted from Venetian glass, very stylish
and comes in 15 different designs
No plumbing in with the thermovit clear glass
rad. Choice of plumbed in or electric for Treese.

Sculpture

WESTLAND LONDON
Westland London are antique dealers
renowned globally for their vast
selection of architectural antiques
displayed to great effect in the Grade
I listed former church with courtyard,
London, EC2. Collections range from
a unique series of sculptures from
The Bank of England, to classical
statues, antique gates, columns,
garden seating, fountains, and finials,
in wood, metal, stone or marble.

View their comprehensive website on:
www.westlandlondon.com
or visit Mon – Fri 9-6, Sat 10-5
St Michael's Church, Leonard Street,
London, EC2A 4QX (Off Great
Eastern street.)
Tube: Old street, Exit 4.
Tel: 020 7739 8094

Cavendish Stone

t: +44 (0)1747 842 214   w: www.cavendishstone.com   e: info@cavendishstone.com

Security

telguard®
Access To Your Home By The Tone Of Your Phone...™

TELGUARD
Units 2/3 The Old Stables
Ockley, Surrey, RH5 5LS
Tel: 01306 710120
Fax: 01306 713769
www.doorentry.co.uk
sales@telguard.co.uk

Telguard is a British company. We
manufacture and distribute our range of
GSM and land line based intercom
systems for entrance doors, gates and
barriers. Control the entrance of your
property from your mobile phone – from
anywhere! We have sales staff and a
network of installers ready to assist you.

Showers

west one bathrooms ltd.

West One Bathrooms Ltd
Destined to created the worlds most
beautiful bathrooms

Please visit our website for more
information and showroom location
www.westonebathrooms.com or
email sales@westonebathrooms.com

Tel: 020 7324 0780

Sinks & Taps

BLANCO
GERMANY

BLANCO UK LIMITED
Tel: 01923 635200
Email: info@blanco.co.uk
Web: www.blanco.co.uk

The BLANCOCULINA-S sets new
standards in tap design. A magnet in
the magnetic hose cradle releases the
splash-free spray hose – and secures it
when not in use. A touch of a button
changes the regular flow to a spray
and back again, and the extra-wide
rotation arc of the spout creates a
number of installation possibilities.
Chrome; high pressure water systems.

Shippers & Packers

Hedley's Humpers

Established in 1973 and with branches
in London, Paris, Avignon and New
York, Hedleys Humpers has built an
enviable reputation for expertise
in packing, shipping, storing and
installing fine art and antiques
throughout the world.

3 St Leonard's Road, North Acton
London NW10 6SX
T: +44 (0)20 8965 8733
F: +44 (0)20 8965 0249
E: london@hedleyshumpers.com
W: www.hedleyshumpers.com

Hedley's Humpers

Spa Facilities

NOLA 7 INTERNATIONAL
Barn 8, Fenton Farm
Crundale
Pembrokeshire SA62 4PY
Freephone: +44 (0) 0808 1201177
Email: wellness@nola7.co.uk
Web: www.nola7.com

At NOLA 7 we always listen to our
clients, embracing their individual
ideas and dreams to develop design
solutions inspired from ancient
civilisations to boutique & specialist
thermal marine hydrotherapy spas.
We take pride in every project and
endeavour to create a soothing
sanctuary to be enjoyed by all. Aroma
Sauna, Rose Steam, Himalayan Salt and
Snow & Ice rooms and vitality pools.

Stone Flooring/Finishes

**Natural stone flooring
Marble & granite worktops
Bespoke bathrooms**

Call us on 01452 714 800 or
visit www.montpellier.co.uk

MONTPELLIER
NATURAL STONE FOR EVERY HOME

Stoves

The Ceramic Stove Company

THE CERAMIC STOVE COMPANY
4 Earl Street
Oxford
OX2 0JA
Tel/Fax: +44 (0)1865 245077
Email: info@ceramicstove.com
Web: www.ceramicstove.com

The Ceramic Stove Company
continues to offer a diverse range
of high-quality, high-efficiency,
heat-retaining woodburning
ceramic stoves and ovens from
manufacturers who are concerned
about style, efficiency and the
environment in equal measure.

Suspended Ceilings

KNAUF AMF CEILINGS LTD
Web: www.amfceilings.co.uk

Knauf AMF is a manufacturer of high performance suspended ceiling systems, wall panels, rafts, baffles and associated bespoke products for the global specification market with over 50 years of history. Owned by Knauf, AMF has its head office in Germany with manufacturing plants in Germany and Austria and is represented in a further 80 countries worldwide. We have specification and contractor representatives covering the whole of the UK, with our ceiling systems being supplied through a national network of distributors.

Tiles

atlas concorde

www.atlasconcorde.it
project@atlasconcorde.it

SALES OFFICE
Tel: 0207 3862694
info@recosurfaces.com
www.recosurfaces.com

Reco is the future of waterproof walling. These stunning panels can be installed in a third of the time it would take to tile. No-grout means no-maintenance. All panels 100% recyclable. 10 year guarantee. Designer range / bespoke images and designs available.

RECO LTD
Enterprise House, Priory Road, Freiston, Boston, Lincolnshire, PE22 0JZ

Tile Flooring

Vitruvius Limited
marble, granite, limestone and slate specialists

VITRUVIUS LIMITED
Unit 1, Omicron House, Fircroft Way, Edenbridge, Kent TN8 6EL
Tel: 01732 864156
Fax: 01732 866180
mg@vitruviusltd.co.uk
www.vitruviusltd.co.uk

Vitruvius is a supplier, manufacturer and fixer of all forms of natural stone. The company is based in Kent with its own modern factory and skilled fabricators and fixers. As a company, we strive to make our clients the raison d'etre of our business - we are proud that, after 25 years, we are still working creatively with many of the same private customers, contractors and developers. We are small, professional and committed.

Jacqueline Talbot Designs

Tel: 07876 741 276
info@jacquelinetalbot.co.uk
www.jacquelinetalbotdesigns.com

Contemporary ceramic tiles made to order for kitchens, bathrooms, splashbacks and anywhere else you can think of except floors

Bespoke design service available including changing colours and creating designs from scratch

R.I.M
tile and mosaic boutique

3/11 Chelsea Harbour Design Centre
+44 (0) 207 376 58 20
www.rimdesign.co.uk

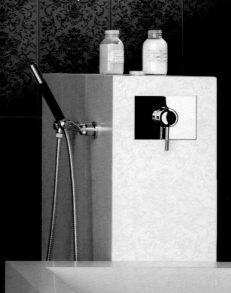

STONE AGE®

T: 020 7384 9090

Upholstered Furniture

Wall Coverings

KINGCOME SOFAS

Tiles of Stow

TILES OF STOW LTD
Langston Priory Workshops,
Station Road, Kingham,
Oxfordshire, OX7 6UP
T: 01608 658993
F: 01608 658951
E: info@tilesofstow.co.uk
W: www.tilesofstow.co.uk

Specialists in the design, manufacture
and hand-decoration of ceramic wall
tiles and tile murals.

Their product range also includes all
types of ceramic, porcelain, glass
and stone wall and floor tiles.

Visit their showroom in the Cotswolds

KINGCOME SOFAS
114 Fulham Road, London, SW3 6HU
Tel: 020 7244 7747
Email: sales@kingcomesofas.co.uk
Web: www.kingcomesofas.co.uk

Kingcome Sofas, known for its
exceptional quality, comfort and
workmanship, is owned by the fabric
and wallpaper company, Colefax and
Fowler.

Kingcome furniture is exclusively
designed and handmade in England,
using only the finest materials. Every
piece is meticulously hand–finished to
meet the exacting demands of each
Kingcome client.

B BROWN DISPLAY MATERIALS
74-78 wood lane end
Hemel Hempstead
Hertfordshire
HP2 4RF
Tel: 08705 340340
Fax: 08705 329610
Email: customerservices@bbrown.co.uk
Web: www.bbrown.co.uk

Original suppliers of display fabrics,
textiles, PVC and polycarbonates for
retail displays and exhibition stands
since 1934.

Backgrounds have been our
background since backgrounds began
and B Brown have more than 400 in
stock.

We now also supply innovative panels
for more feature areas too.

Vases & Sculptures

VIA ARKADIA CHELSEA
3-19/20 Chelsea Harbour Design Centre
London SW10 0XE
Tel: 020 7351 7057
Fax: 020 7351 7087
mail@via-arkadia.co.uk

VIA ARKADIA HAMPSTEAD
84 Heath Street
Hampstead
London NW3 1DN
Tel: 020 7794 2341
Fax: 056 0344 1582
hampsteadtiles@via-arkadia.co.uk

Via Arkadia Ltd is an experienced tile
supplier of top quality Italian stone,
marble, porcelain, ceramic, mosaics and
many other materials serving both the
professional and domestic markets.
See ranges on our website:
www.via-arkadia.co.uk

**MURASPEC DECORATIVE
SOLUTIONS LTD**
Tel: 08705 117 118
Fax: 08705 329 020
customerservices@muraspec.com
www.muraspec.com
Facebook: facebook.com/muraspec
Twitter: twitter.com/Muraspec

Muraspec is a leading British designer,
manufacturer and distributor of
wallcoverings for commercial and
residential use worldwide. With over
125 years of British heritage, our name
is synonymous with inspiring design,
high quality and excellent service. We
also sell decorative surfaces solutions
such as Lumicor and Impressions panels.

Tradescant & Son

TEXTILES AND WALLPAPER

Digital inspiration...

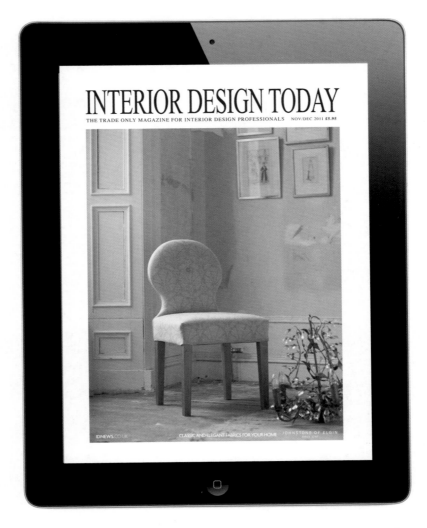

Download your free app today, and read your favourite interiors magazine on the go.

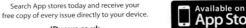

Wall Hangings & Paintings

EASYART
Unit 301/302
Hatton Square Business Centre
16/16A Baldwins Gardens
London EC1N 7RJ
Tel: +44 (0)203 176 0946
clare.harries@easyart.com
www.easyart.com/business

Easyart makes buying art inspiring and easy, working with leading artists and designers to publish the best range of prints available and beautiful UK custom framing for all budgets. Our print-on demand service allows us to print a variety of sizes and media including canvas. Projects include private, leisure and corporate interiors.

Wallpaper

WALLPAPERDIRECT
Tel: 01323 430886
Email: info@wallpaperdirect.co.uk
Web: www.wallpaperdirect.co.uk

wallpaperdirect.co.uk offers the widest range of wallpaper and wallcoverings online. The website brings together over 9,000 wallpaper designs from top brands including Sanderson, Harlequin, Osborne & Little, Albany and Designers Guild as well as specialist brands not found on the high street. Fabrics, curtains, bedding and lighting are also available on the website and for paint just visit sister site - designerpaint.co.uk

Windows, Doors & Shutters

CRITTALL WINDOWS LIMITED
Francis House, Freebournes Road,
Witham, Essex, CM8 3UN
Tel 01376 530800
Fax 01376 530801
E-mail: hq@crittall-windows.co.uk
Website: www.crittall-windows.com

Crittall designed and manufactured the first standard steel windows in the 1920's. Today's units replicate that same classic elegant slimline styling whilst offering superb thermal performance that meets the latest requirements of Part L of the Building Regulations. With hot dipped galvanising and a Duralife polyester powder coat finish, maintenance is kept a minimum.

Designed to preserve *your* style

Selectaglaze secondary glazing offers:

- *Purpose Made and Discrete*
- *Superb Thermal Insulation*
- *Excellent Draught Proofing*
- *The Most Effective Method of Sound Proofing*
- *Reversible Adaptation*
- *Secured by Design Option*

Secondary Glazing is suitable for all types of Heritage Building

improving our environment ™

Tel: 01727 837271 www.selectaglaze.co.uk

steel reinforced entrance and internal feature doors

e: info@urbanfront.co.uk   www.urbanfront.co.uk   t: 01494 778 787

KLOEBER UK LTD
West Newlands Industrial Estate
Somersham
Cambs
PE28 3EB
Tel: 01487 740044
Fax: 01487 740404
Info@kloeber.co.uk
www.kloeber.co.uk

Kloeber UK Ltd is an innovative
manufacturer of bespoke glazing
solutions in timber, aluminium and
composite and a market leader in
folding sliding doors, windows and
entrance doors. Kloeber are the only
company to have accredited Secured by
Design on their timber bi fold doors.

LONGDEN
55 Parkwood Road, Sheffield,
South Yorkshire, S3 8AH
Tel: 0114 270 6330
enquiries@longdendoors.co.uk
www.longdendoors.co.uk

The Longden range of hardwood
panelled door sets, manufactured in
Britain, combines the highest quality
of traditional craftsmanship with the
performance levels needed to meet
today's technical criteria.
The majority of door styles can
offer performance characteristics of
fire-resistance up to FD60 and
sound reduction of 18-37RwdB.

Unit 1, Wheaton Road, Witham,
Essex CM8 3UJ
Tel 01376 534 700
www.junckers.co.uk

Naturally warm underfoot, durable
and long-lasting, Junckers' solid,
pre-finished hardwood floors are
available in a rich and varied list of
timbers and finishes, which now
includes their new Texture & Colour
Design Collection.

Wood & Laminate Flooring

LEADERFLUSH SHAPLAND
Milnhay Road, Langley Mill,
Nottingham, NG16 4AZ
Tel: 01773 530500
Fax: 01773 530040
enquiries@leaderflushshapland.co.uk
www.leaderflushshapland.co.uk

Leaderflush Shapland the UK's leading
performance doorset manufacturer, part
of SIG Plc a successful £3 billion
company offers a wide range of bespoke
doors and doorsets. Performance
characteristics include fire resistance,
sound reduction, radiation shielding and
security, making the range one of the
most comprehensive in the marketplace.

EBONY AND CO
15 Savile Row, Mayfair, London
W1S 3PJ
t. +44(0)20 7734 0734
e. london@ebonyandco.com
w. www.ebonyandco.com

Ebony and Co is an international
team of dedicated professionals,
passionate about our unique
product – the finest handcrafted
wood flooring on the planet. We
deliver an infinite range of designs
through a complete 'forest to
floor' service, flowing from the
individual tree to the final fit,
finish and then beyond.

THE WEST SUSSEX ANTIQUE
TIMBER COMPANY LTD
Reliance Works, Newpound,
Wisborough Green,
West Sussex, RH14 0AZ
Tel: 01403 700 139
Fax: 01403 700 936
Web: www.wsatimber.co.uk
Email: wsatimber@aol.com

The West Sussex Antique Timber
Company Ltd supply the best traditional
solid oak floors from sustainable
sources, they can supply and fit random
width oak flooring from 150mm to
280mm wide, compatible with all types
of underfloor heating, stained with their
own antique oil stains. They also
specialise in parquetry, structural timber
repairs, oak trusses and barns and offer
a complete in house joinery service.

XYLO CLEAF
thermo / structured / surface

EMOTION WITHIN REACH

A decorative paper printed with high-resolution wood grains, abstract designs or solid colours to either one or both surfaces of the panel. The papers are treated with melamine resins that, under heat and pressure, actually become part of the panel itself – thus the term "Thermo Structured Surface" (TSS).

TSS is used to produce office, hotel, restaurant, healthcare and residential furniture, retail displays, kitchen & bathroom units, wardrobes, wall panelling, internal doors. The distinctive features of CLEAF material are its durability, its decorative texture and its easy-to-maintain surface.

Quality, efficiency, research and sensitivity to markets and trends contribute to a continuing success and constant evolution of CLEAF material, in terms of technology and design.

Xylo House, Unit 13, Brunswick Industrial Park, Brunswick Way, New Southgate, London N11 1JL
T +44(0) 20 8368 8122   F +44(0) 20 8368 8127   info@xylocleaf.com   www.xylocleaf.com

HEADINGS A-Z